The Instrument Pilot's Library
• Volume Four •

On the Approach

by
The Editors of *IFR* and *IFR Refresher*

Belvoir Publications, Inc.
Greenwich, Connecticut

ISBN: 1-879620-22-7

Printed and bound in the United States of America by Arcata Graphics, Fairfield, Pennsylvania.

Contents

Preface

The fourth volume of the *Instrument Pilot's Library* looks at the portion of IFR flight that gets more attention than any other: The approach.

There's a great deal to talk about when dealing with instrument approaches. We could easily have filled a book with just the material we've done covering the intricacies of individual approaches around the country, but that would have left out what you, the pilot, really need to know: The information on how things work and how to make the process work for you.

We do examine individual approaches, to be sure, but we also include information on how to go about flying approaches smoothly and easily. There are specific techniques for glideslope and localizer tracking, descent to landing, flying circling approaches, and more.

The book is divided into four sections: First up is coverage of the approach that most of us fly the most often: The ILS. We'll "fly" a sample approach and see how it's possible to stay ahead of the game simply by knowing how ATC gets you from the en route portion of your flight onto the final approach course.

The second section covers non-precision approaches of all sorts, both their similarities and differences. We'll discuss the future of approaches, which at present seems solidly rooted in GPS.

Third comes topics covering the end of the approach, from circling maneuvers to descent from the MDA to downwind landings.

Last is a section containing a variety of useful tips on other aspects of flying approaches, including discussions of DME arcs, ATC "tricks," and finally a discussion of maintaining positional awareness.

We hope you find this information insightful, fresh, and useful in your flying.

• Section One •

Precision Approaches

The "Complex" ILS

Pilots often think of the ILS as the most "complex" approach there is, since it provides precision guidance to the missed approach point. The only other system that can do that at present is MLS, which is dead in its tracks. There have been demonstrations of differential GPS precision approaches, too, but so far that's as far as satellite-based precision approaches have gotten.

But the ILS isn't really complicated. In fact, flying an ILS approach is a good deal easier than a typical NDB approach, not only because of the more precise guidance the ILS signal provides, but in large part because of the comparatively simple, straightforward displays the pilot uses to find his way to the airport.

The Uncomplicated Approach

A flight examiner was once brought up sharply during the otherwise flawless portion of an IFR-rating flight test when, as an afterthought, he said to the keen, young candidate, "By the way, just what does 'ILS' stand for?"

Without hesitation, the applicant replied, "I'll Land Safely."

This answer expressed a thoroughgoing confidence in the power of the instrument landing system to get a harried pilot down in good order when the weather is at even the most minimal minimums. His instructor had encouraged him in his faith.

And rightly so (with one big qualification): after all, an ILS may allow you to descend to as low as 200 feet above the surface, giving you a much better prospect for breaking out in time to land safely. An airport with an ILS is a far more promising alternate than one with only a non-precision approach, especially when conditions are low or lowering over a broad area. An ILS alternate allows standard minimums 200 feet lower than its non-precision counterpart. The system provides *precise electronic* information and guidance about your relationship to the glideslope (hence its classification) and the missed approach point (MAP).

Furthermore, the ILS is a refreshingly easy approach to fly.

"I'll Land Safely" is therefore a good attitude with which to approach an ILS (no pun intended). The major qualification we noted above, however, is that no ILS guarantees a safe and legal landing. It will take you lower in the soup, but if the bouillabaisse is still out there at decision height, there's nothing for it but to accept a missed approach—even if you have the needles neatly crossed and centered.

Precision and Intimidation

Yet some pilots—students and rated IFR airmen alike—view the ILS as an ultimate challenge full of threats and embarrassments. They see the sensitivity of the localizer and glideslope needles as a technological adversary and their progress down final as a dogfight in which the needles are targets taking purposeful evasive action. Training, experience and improved proficiency can eliminate that sense of intimidation, for its causes lie not in the system but in ourselves.

The needles aren't there to be chased, but to be controlled. In fact, even when the air is troubled, we shall see how the ILS is constructed to make precise guidance the pilot's ally.

A Familiar Concept

What makes the ILS different from non-precision approaches is its nature from the final approach fix to the MAP, the point at which the pilot must choose to land or fly the missed approach. Until then, the approach is constructed along the same principles as those of VOR and NDB approaches, with segments designed to establish the aircraft at the FAF on the right heading and at the right altitude to transition smoothly to a comfortable descent toward the runway. Depending on the design of the particular approach, there will be an initial and/or intermediate segment to do just that. These may involve a procedure turn or a holding pattern in place of a procedure turn to give you room and time to slow to your approach speed, set up the airplane for the landing, descend in comfortable increments to intercept the glideslope and establish yourself on a workable final approach course heading.

The nearly universal advent of radar vectoring makes these early steps even easier, often to the point of eliminating them (there are many ILSes at busier airports where, even though a procedure turn is charted it is never, ever actually flown), though vectoring can create problems of its own.

If the approach includes a compass locator (an NDB) at the outer marker, the task of visualizing your position with respect to the OM and localizer is lightened still more as you intercept the localizer. If you are being vectored, your ADF and/or your basic visualization of your position will, in a majority of cases, reveal that your ground track will closely resemble that of an aircraft making a standard VFR approach complete with downwind, base and final approach legs.

And just as you would select an aiming point on the runway and set up a glidepath to it during a visual approach, you will do the same thing on the ILS, except that the aiming point is, or should be, the center of the doughnut on your ILS head. The difference is that you must fly with a steady and fine touch, adjusting to and maintaining your pitch, heading and power with more precision than if you were to have the runway in sight, sprawling in front of you.

The Anatomy

A typical ILS consists of five interrelated parts that provide positional guidance. The two centerpieces are the localizer and glideslope; the uninitiated believe that these are a single "beam" that goes out along the centerline of the ILS, but in fact the localizer and glideslope are two completely separate signals of different frequencies, transmitted from different facilities located thousands of feet from one another, and picked up by separate antennas on the airplane. The only place they come together is on the face of the nav head in the cockpit.

For *lateral* guidance, there is the localizer, which varies in width from 3° to 6°, depending on the distance between the transmitter antenna and the landing threshold (the localizer transmitter is located beyond the far end of the runway, typically about a thousand feet from the departure end). The angular width of the localizer is tailored to provide an actual width of 700 feet at the landing threshold. That means that a full-scale needle deflection can be anywhere from 1.5°-3° off the final approach course. That's far more sensitive than an ordinary VOR (four times as sensitive, in fact), but sensitivity connotes precision, which translates into lower minimums.

Also, the precision goes up as one gets closer to the airport: At the outer marker—four to seven miles from the end of the runway—each dot of a five-dot indicator represents roughly 300 feet. At the middle marker—3,000 to 6,000 feet from the threshold—each dot represents about 100 feet.

The Convergence Factor

If you keep the localizer needle centered, on breakout you will see the runway directly ahead, aligned within 3° of the final approach course. (Not all ILSes go "straight down the barrel:" a built-in offset of one or two degrees is allowed for terrain and other considerations. If this is the case, it's called an "offset localizer" and is noted as such on the approach plate's profile view.)

The lateral shape of the glidepath, then, is that of a narrowing chute. Since the signals diverge as they radiate from the localizer transmitter—as do a VOR's radials—they of course converge inbound. If you are, say, two dots off center at the outer marker and keep the needle there as you fly down the localizer, you will actually be nearing the centerline as you approach the middle marker. You want to put the needle in the doughnut, of course, but the convergence factor means that you needn't rush to center the needle to stay on a ball-park course to the runway threshold.

Off-course localizer indications are usable within 10° of the centerline up to 18 miles from the transmitter and within 35° of the centerline within 10 miles of the transmitter (remember that the transmitter is a quarter mile or so beyond the *far end* of the runway). Since needle readings may be unreliable more than 35° off the centerline, the indications can become confusing when you're being vectored for an ILS, especially if you're downwind and abeam of the airport.

Localizer frequencies lie within the same range as those of terminal VORs, 108.1-111.95 MHz, and are always on "odd tenth" channels, such as 108.1, 108.15, 108.3, 108.35, etc. The signals are received by the same equipment that receives VOR signals, and the CDI responds to them in the same way (though the actual decoding circuitry is different). When you tune your VOR/ILS receiver to an ILS, the OBS is functionless.

The four-letter ILS indentifier is always begun with the letter "I." Keep in mind that ATC can talk over ILS frequencies. If you lose your comm receivers, you can fall back on the ILS and use your transponder's ident button to respond.

Should the system's glideslope fail, you can still shoot an approach via the localizer, albeit at higher minimums. The ILS approach plate will describe the glideslope-out approach.

The Glideslope

The addition of the glideslope could be said to change the chute into a funnel. As with the localizer, the glideslope's signals diverge as they radiate from the transmitting antenna, which is located abeam the fixed distance marker, about 1,000 feet from the threshold (the transmitter, itself, is located in the familiar red-and-white checkered shack next to the antenna mast). Thus, if you remain a dot or two above or below the centerline as you descend, your path will converge with the center of the glideslope.

Never allow yourself to remain below the center of the glideslope. FAR 91.129 stipulates that large and turbine-powered aircraft must fly at or above the glideslope—a smart practice for small airplanes, too.

FAA's diagram of the ILS (found in the AIM) may suggest that the glideslope will guide you safely to the fixed distance marker (the large white runway markings that denote the intersection of the glideslope with the runway surface) but that is definitely not the case, which is one reason why ducking below decision height in the blind is dangerous. Below the DH, the glideslope signal can become confusing and will actually "flare out" between 18 and 27 feet above the runway.

The ILS glideslope is usually at a 3° angle to the horizontal, about the same angle set by the VASI lights. The glideslope signal is much narrower than the localizer signal: 1.4° full-scale up to full-scale down. It's normally usable down to about one wingspan above the runway.

There are some inherent problems with ILS signals. Be alert for "false" glideslopes, which can be received at altitudes above the proper GS. Similarly, just as a localizer signal may be transmitted in the opposite direction from the ILS, so may GS signals be emitted in that direction. While the localizer signal may be used for a back-course approach (if one is published), any glideslope reception on the "wrong" side of the airport *must be ignored.*

The glideslope signal frequencies (UHF in the 330 MHz range) are paired with localizer frequencies and are automatically selected when the localizer is tuned in. However, it is picked up by a separate UHF receiver which may be part of the panel radio, itself, or may be installed elsewhere in the airplane. The antenna, too, is separate: usually it's mounted on the belly, and takes the form of a flat plate or small fin.

If DME is provided with the ILS, it will indicate the distance to touchdown. Manually tuned DMEs must be set to the localizer frequency.

On an ILS, the missed approach point is designated by a specific altitude along the glideslope. When you reach that height, if you don't see either the runway *or* the approach lights, you must immediately initiate the missed approach. No ducking under for a peek, no leveling out at the DH (this is distinctly different from a non-precision approach)—you must immediately climb out according to the published missed approach procedure. The good news is that ILS missed approaches are infrequent. The bad news is that when one becomes necessary, things happen fast, so fly the ILS *expecting and prepared* to fly the missed.

Other Guidance

The localizer and glideslope tell you where you are in the funnel leading to the runway—wide, high or low. Other ILS components—the outer and middle markers, the compass locator and the approach lighting system mark your passage past the key points along the final approach course.

The outer marker is located approximately 4 to 7 miles from the runway, just about where the glideslope is intercepted at the intermediate segment altitude. The outer marker can also serve as a final approach fix, but only for a non-precision approach.

The middle marker is approximately a half-mile from the threshold, at a position corresponding to the point at which the glideslope reaches decision height.

The outer marker (OM) and middle marker (MM) signals are received by a single-frequency radio that is permanently tuned to 75 MHz, the frequency on which not only the outer and middle markers, but other marker beacons in the system (inner, fan, and back course) transmit. The display is a series of three lights: blue for the OM, amber for the MM and white for the IM (if present). Also, there's a distinct series of beeps as each marker is passed.

Most marker beacon receivers have a test function, which should be used before every IFR flight (it proves the receiver is working, and besides, the passengers like seeing all the colored lights).

Marker beacon receivers have a "high" and "low" sensitivity setting. We recommend using the "low" setting, since "high" expands the area of reception and reduces your ability to pinpoint passage over the marker. Note, however, that the outer and middle markers *do not* actually represent the point of glideslope intercept or the MAP: they are merely aids to alert you that you're very close. In fact, you can fly an ILS quite legally without a marker beacon receiver.

Where the Descent Begins

When you pass over the outer marker, the beacon receiver will flash a blue light and the audio (speaker, headset, or both, depending on how you've set it up) will emit two dashes per second (- - - -). You may have been asked by ATC to "report the (outer) marker," but don't regard the OM as the final approach fix. Your descent to the runway should begin when you intercept and begin to follow the glideslope, whether this happens just outside the marker (usually) or inside it. Note also that if the OM is out of service, the landing minimums remain unchanged.

Not so for an out-of-service middle marker. If the DH is 200 feet above touchdown, it will increase by 50 feet if the MM goes out of service—regardless of whether the failure is in the ground equipment or in the airplane. When no middle marker is installed, the DH will be 250 rather than the usual 200 feet. However, for those ILSes that have a DH 250 feet above touchdown, the lack of a middle marker does not raise the DH.

When you reach the middle marker, you'll be from 3,000 to 6,000 feet from the runway threshold. Most likely about 3,500. Your marker beacon receiver will show an amber light, and the audio will sound off with alternating dots and dashes repeated 95 times per minute (-.-.-.-.).

Again, the middle marker does not define the MAP. If you're flying the glideslope, the missed approach is dictated by your reaching decision height. If you're only using the localizer, the MAP is defined by a specific time from the FAF at your groundspeed as published on the approach plate. The MM is a backup indicator. If you're in the blind and below the DH when the MM is reached, you've busted the minimum and could be in even worse trouble than the legal kind. *Decision* height means just that: At that altitude, don't wait, *decide* and fly the missed approach, if it's called for.

The marker beacon receiver also has a white light. This can indicate passage over the inner marker, which is installed at the DH position for Category II ILSes. Cat IIs allow specially equipped and certified aircraft to use minimums lower than the usual Cat I ILS. The light is accompanied by a series of 360 dots per minute (......).

Compass Locators

These are a boon to flexibility and efficiency. Compass locators are NDBs with a power output of less than 25 watts and a range of about 15 miles, depending on the beacon and the direction of the signal. Compass locators are usually co-located with outer markers, hence the term LOM, or locator-outer marker. Their identifiers are the first two letters of the ILS identifier—if the localizer identifier is "IBAF" (Westfield, Mass.) the LOM is "BA."

On occasion, you may come upon a locator-middle marker (LMM); its identifier will be the last two letters of the localizer identifier—for "IJFK," "FK."

A LOM can allow direct clearance to the outer marker, definitely a time and hassle-saving grace. When you are being vectored, monitoring the bearing to the LOM on your ADF is invaluable for tracking your position, especially during localizer intercepts.

Rabbit Runs

Approach light systems (ALS) hold for IFR pilots the joy that there is, in fact, a way down through the clag. On a close approach, you will most likely see the avenue of lights before you see your goal, the runway. Not seeing them (or the runway) by the time you've reached the MAP means a missed approach. For those who've experienced it, there's nothing quite like catching sight of the lights just as you're about to shove the throttle(s) in for the missed approach.

Perhaps the most fascinating component of the system is the "rabbit," the pulse of light that appears to streak towards the runway either beyond the main part of the ALS (RAIL) or within it (sequenced flashers).

FAR 91.175 sets forth the criteria for continuing an ILS below the DH. At the DH, you must have a least one of the following in sight:

- The approach lighting system;
- The runway threshold, its markings or its lights;
- The runway end identifier lights (REIL, not RAIL);
- The VASI;
- The touchdown zone, touchdown zone markings or lights;
- The runway, its markings or its lights.

You must also have the flight visibility specified for the procedure being flown. If the ALS or RAIL is out of service, the visibility minimums increase. Part 135 or 121 pilots may not even begin an approach if the field is *reporting* below minimums. If you're a private operator (Part 91), you may at least attempt the approach, however grim the report. If you can see the approach lights through the windshield, not just from the side window, you probably have the required visibility.

In the next chapter, we'll delve further into the questions of reported visibility and how to judge them, along with techniques for flying the ILS from approach clearance to runway contact.

In this chapter, we've laid out the apparently complex structure of what is, in truth, a simple system. The emphasis placed on precision during the final descent creates an aura of technological and operational intricacy. Still, the ILS is at heart similar to other approaches: It calls for flying certain courses and altitudes, albeit with great precision, and making a basic decision at a key point as to whether to land or do the IFR equivalent of a go-around. If calls for alertness and some radio dexterity, as we shall see next month, but in essence, the business end of an ILS is a stable funnel with devices to let you know where you are.

This most "complex" of approaches is really not so complex after all. It can be flown easily: How easily, we'll discuss in the next chapter.

The instrument landing system is an under-appreciated technical marvel. In its ultimate evolution, the Cat IIIc, an ILS is capable of guiding an airplane not just to the runway threshold, but practically right onto the centerline, sometimes in visibility that's too poor for a following vehicle to find the airplane.

Not many of us have flown a IIIc autoland but even a humble Cat I system capable of 200 and a half is a remarkable navaid. There aren't many days when it won't bring you home. The ILS is so reliable, in fact, that it's taken for granted and, as a result, certain misunderstandings about how the system works persist.

ILS Myths

We mentioned Myth 1 earlier in the chapter. It's one of the most widely held, so let's take a closer look here.

Myth 1: The ILS signal is a single beam

While it's probably acceptable to visualize the localizer and glideslope as "beams" in space, that's not really what they are. For one thing, the localizer and glideslope are entirely separate systems, with separate signals. It's more accurate to think of the LOC and GS as intersecting planes in space, with the on-course path precisely along the juncture of the two planes.

Rather than being formed by a beam, the localizer and slope are each formed by a phase resolution or a superposition of a carrier modulated at two different audio frequencies. In concept, the system is not unlike a VASI except that instead of the pilot sensing the on-course path as a juxtaposition of two different colored lights, the LOC and GS receivers listen for the correct electronic blend of signals that indicate on-course.

In simple terms, here's how the localizer and glideslope transmitters work: Using phased array antennas, the transmitters emit signals on the assigned ILS frequency. On one side of the array, the signal is modulated at 90hz, the other at 150hz. In the case of the localizer, the 90hz signal represents the fly-right signal, the 150hz signal is used for fly-left. On-course—the localizer centerline—consists of an equal blend of 90hz and 150hz. When the localizer receiver senses this, it displays the output as a centered CDI.

Interestingly, the 90hz and 150hz modulations are musical tones so theoretically, a musician or anyone with good musical pitch could fly the localizer by ear, assuming hearing good enough to distinguish tones at the lower limit of human hearing. You can sometimes hear the tones; just turn up the localizer audio as you taxi or fly across the runway centerline. You'll hear the tone change as you cross from the 90hz segment to the 150hz area or vice versa.

If you could hear the glideslope audio, you could do the same thing, since the GS transmitter works on the identical principle but is tuned to represent a much narrower on-course indication. On the glideslope, the 90Hz signal is fly-up, the 150hz signal is fly-down. On a typical system, a glideslope course is 1.4 degrees wide vertically or about 742 feet edge-to-edge at an outer marker placed 5 miles from the runway. A localizer, by comparison, is about 5 degrees wide or nearly 3000 feet at the marker.

Myth 2: Pilots need to be on the alert for false localizers and glideslopes.

Many pilots have been somewhat startled to see ILS on-course indications (with no flags) many miles from what they know to be the correct course. This is because many systems transmit false localizers and all have false glideslopes.

It's technically possible for false localizers to exist up to 90 degrees from the actual course alignment and there may be more than one false signal. The false localizers may show correct or reverse needle sensing.

Because some glideslopes transmit an accurate, usable signal well beyond the 35-degree width of the localizer signal, it's possible to get a good glideslope indication with a false localizer indication.

Does this mean you could be vectored onto the wrong localizer or fly the incorrect course after completing a transition? Not likely. False localizers are extremely narrow and the signal strength is often so weak that the CDI needle would behave strangely enough to alert the pilot. In any case, double-checking your position with ADF, DME or loran before turning inbound on a localizer will certainly clue you in to the existence of a false signal. On a transition, stick to the published procedures and altitudes and you won't go wrong.

False glideslopes *always* exist above the true slope. But the systems are flight checked rigorously for the existence of false glideslopes below the true signal. If you ever catch a false signal from above, you'll know it. It'll descend at about 6 degrees (or more) and you'll probably need full flaps, gear down, near-idle power and an ear-shattering descent rate to stay with it. Best advice here is to always intercept the glideslope at the posted intercept altitude and always crosscheck the posted marker crossing altitude.

Myth 3: Unmonitored ILSs could transmit dangerously false signals.

Occasionally, in the notams, you'll see the phrase "ILS 32

unmonitored," or something similiar. Some pilots take this to mean that you fly the approach at your own risk since it could be transmitting erroneous signals.

In truth, all ILSs are equipped with executive monitors that continuously sample signal quality. When an out-of-tolerance condition develops, the monitors shut the system down.

"Unmonitored" means that the navaid status is not necessarily reported to ATC or FSS. That means ATC may assign the approach without knowing if it's on the air. It's up the pilot to determine if the signal is flyable. That means checking the LOC identifier and making sure there aren't any flags.

Myth 4: There's no way to cockpit-check LOC and GS receivers.

The FARs are surprisingly liberal with regard to required avionics equipment checks. The transponder has to be checked every 24 months and the VORs every 30 days, yet there's no such requirement for LOC and GS receivers. This seems illogical, since flying an ILS gets you much closer to the terrain than droning along the airway. That doesn't mean you can't cockpit-check the LOC and GS, however.

There are a couple of ways to check the localizer receiver. One is to simply taxi into position on the centerline with the localizer tuned and check the needle alignment. It should be dead center, within perhaps a 1/2 dot to either side.

Another method is to taxi across the width of the runway at the threshold. The needle should displace approximately one dot (or 20 percent of full scale) for every 70 feet of course displacement, thus on a 150-foot wide runway, the needle would swing from one dot left to one dot right or vice versa. Another variation of this check is to fly parallel to the runway, crossing the threshold precisely over the left or right edge of the runway. The needle should show a 1/5 scale deflection, or about a dot.

A good before-takeoff check of the glideslope is to make sure it shows a full fly-up signal when you're in position for departure near the approach threshold. In the air, intercept the GS at the posted altitude and check the marker crossing altitude. It should agree within 50 feet of the published figure. If it doesn't, check your altimeter setting and/or have both the altimeter and receiver checked. In extremely cold weather, you may notice a significant error that's neither the altimeter nor the receiver's fault. In that case, you'll have to correct the altimeter for temperature error.

Myth 5: Nervous needle movement is often due to course roughness, not pilot technique.

In an ideal world, ILSs would be installed only at airports in flat terrain unobstructed by hills, trees, buildings, towers and other natural and manmade objects. In reality, these objects are almost always present and they have some effect on ILS signal quality.

This interference is called course roughness. It generally shows up as nervous or unexpected CDI or glideslope needle movement. While it's true that many ILSs do have course roughness, the amount of allowable roughness is quite small. From a point 4 miles from the runway to about 3500 feet from the threshold, the allowable roughness tapers from one dot of deflection to about 1/2 dot. Inside of that distance, a course won't pass flight check if it exhibits more than about a needle width of roughness.

What this means to the pilot is that roughness is such a minor factor as to be unnoticeable in many circumstances. If the needles are dancing around more than they should, chances are the problem is pilot technique, a loose or corroded antenna or receiver in need of attention.

Flying a Typical ILS

Every approach is different, but in a sense they're all the same. The details of weather conditions, aircraft equipment, pilot state of mind (and body), traffic volume, and secondary approach features may change, but in the end the same tasks are always performed in much the same order.

In the last chapter we took a close look at how the ILS works; now let's fly one, going through the motions to see just what you should be doing, and when you should be doing it.

For our sample approach we've picked one very familiar to a lot of pilots, the ILS 16 at White Plains, New York. There's nothing tricky about this approach (we've saved those for later in the book), but it's a challenge nonetheless, due to the highly congested airspace that surrounds the airport. There's lots of traffic about, the Class B area directly overhead, and controllers who can outtalk the fastest auctioneer in the land.

The ILS and its Golden Rules

When the ILS first became part of the instrument repertory in World War II, it was seen by many pilots as a wonder. Decades later, the instrument landing system is still our best means of making precise approaches. As we pointed out in the first chapter, the system is not only loaded with means of providing vital information in the blind, it's also fairly easy to fly.

There are two essential jobs involved in handling an ILS: Flying attitude precisely and organizing the airplane efficiently. Flying attitude is the same as for all phases of instrument flight—using the control and performance instruments to establish and hold the right altitudes, headings, airspeeds and rates of climb and descent. The ILS

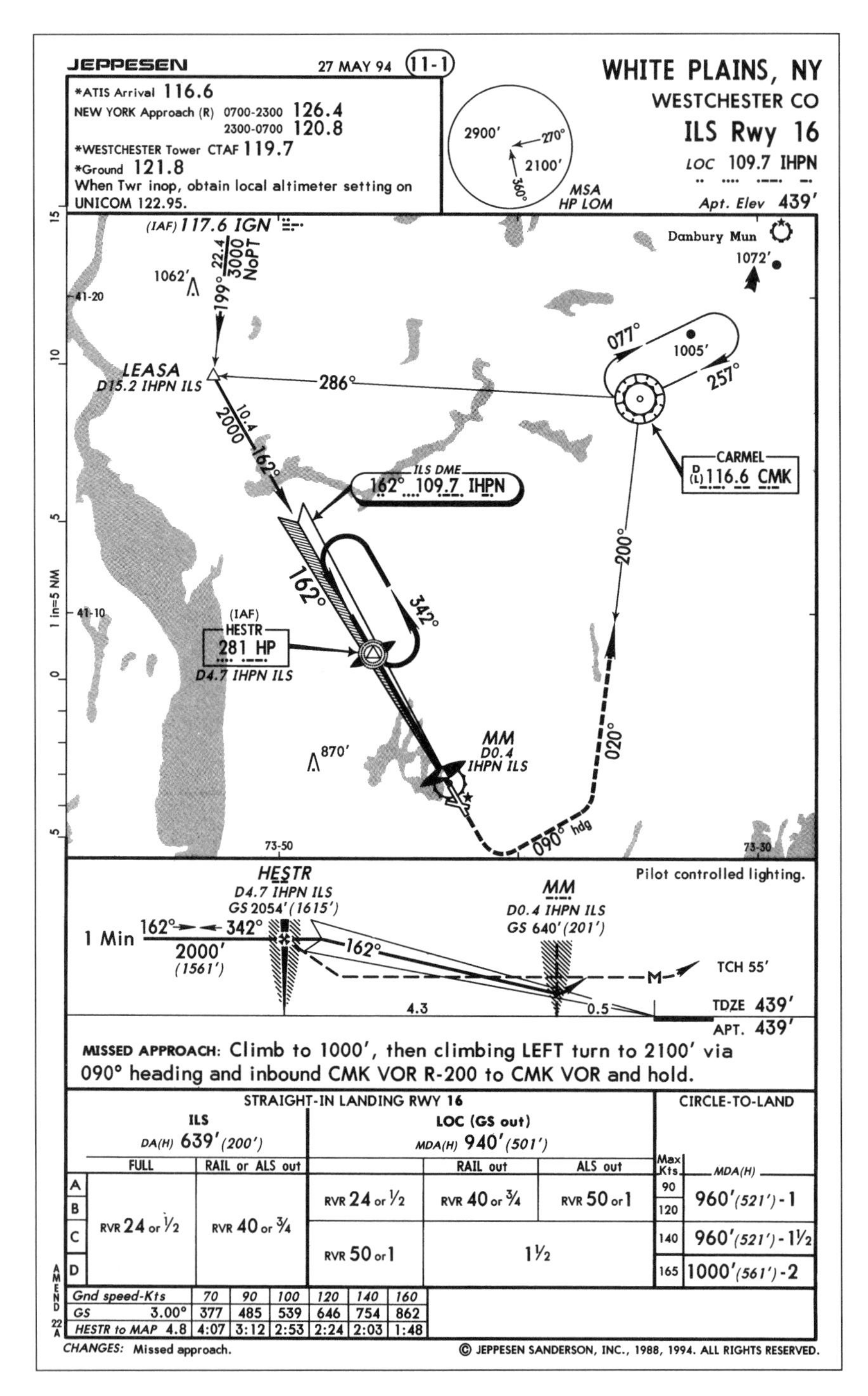

© 1994 Jeppesen-Sanderson, Inc. Reproduced with permission. NOT FOR NAVIGATION.

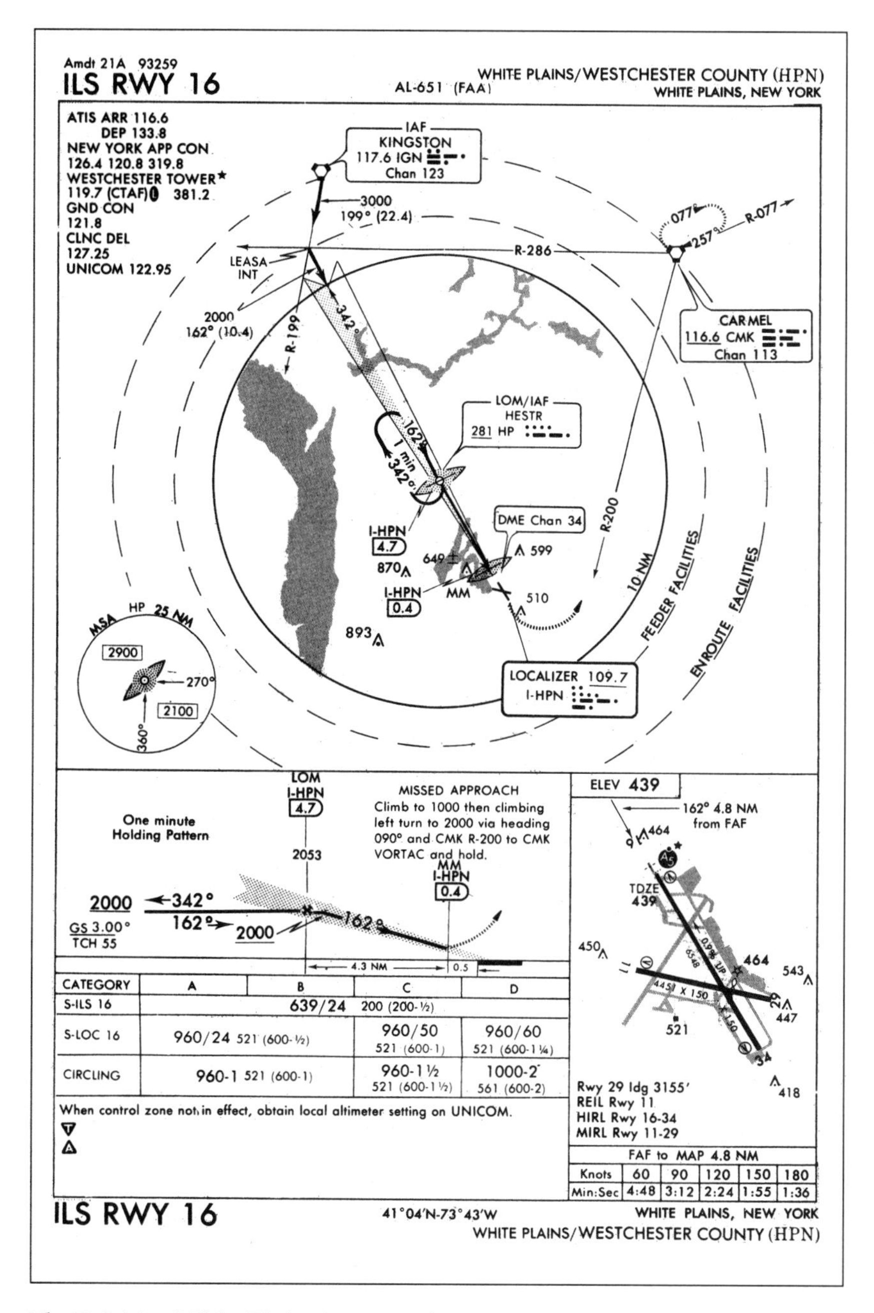

The ILS 16 at White Plains is a typical precision approach into a busy general aviation field. HPN provides airline service to supplement Newark, LaGuardia and JFK. The result is a traffic mix that includes both Cessna 152s and B 737s.

needles may be quite sensitive, but not more than an alert scan and steady hands can control.

According to FAR Part 91, if you are not given vectors to the localizer, you are required to fly the courses and maintain the altitudes indicated on the approach plate. (These initial and intermediate phases are the same as for non-precision approaches.)

Still, especially at busy airports, the more likely timesaving possibility is that you will be given vectors, which means that you may have to work fast to keep up.

Organizing the Approach

Let's say that your approach will be to Runway 16 at White Plains, New York. You are arriving at the terminal area from the east, and have been told to expect vectors to the localizer. You're flying the usual (but unpublished) transition that goes from the Bridgeport, CT VOR along the 289° radial to RYMES intersection, located near Carmel VOR (CMK). You know from the plate and your present position that you'll be effectively flying a left traffic pattern as Approach vectors you onto the localizer.

Organizing your airplane (say, a Lance) begins with pulling out the plate and setting up the radios. You can use the radio stack, itself, as your checklist, starting from the top:

- Audio panel—set and test the marker beacon receiver.
- Comm 1—tuned to New York Approach on 126.4.
- Comm 2—tuned to the tower frequency, 119.7.
- Nav 1—tuned to the localizer, IHPN (109.7); the OBS is set for the ILS 162° course, as a memory aid (remember from the last chapter that the OBS has no function on an ILS).
- Nav 2—set to 116.6, Carmel VOR (CMK), from which you've taken the latest ATIS information. CMK is important also because you will go there to hold if you must fly the missed approach; since you will approach the vortac on the 200° radial, set the OBS to the inbound course of 020°.
- The ADF is tuned to 281 (HP), the Hestr compass locator, which will figure prominently as you monitor your position.

Your aircraft is now *almost* set up for the first part of the approach, but there will be more to do.

At this point, you should be committing vital information to memory, for you don't want to have to consult the approach plate at the crucial stages of the approach—on the final segment and at the start of the missed approach, if there is one.

On your lapboard or on a sheet you can clip to the yoke—to avoid excessive head movements while scanning—write down the fundamental numbers you need to have in mind. Yes, they're printed right there on the chart, but writing them down will accomplish a couple of things: First, it will separate them from the chart's clutter and set them aside so you can see them at a glance; second, the very act of reading them and writing them down will help you commit them to memory. Saying them aloud a few times also helps, we find.

If you were flying the full published approach—and as a backup in case of comm loss (when you would have to fly the full approach)—you would need: the heading (H) of the final approach course; the altitude (A) of the procedure turn and the intermediate segments and the altitude at decision height; the time (T) from the LOM to the missed approach point (in case of sudden glideslope loss, when the approach would become a localizer approach); and the initial, *do it now* portion of the missed approach procedure—what you don't have time to look up when you begin the missed approach. (Unlikely in this case; HPN is a busy radar airport, and they want you out of the way as fast as possible; we've never met anyone who's had to fly the full approach.)

On your note pad, the information might look like this:

H - 162°
A - 2,000 (PT alt)
  639 (DH)
T - 3:12 (LOM to DH)
MAP - **UP** to 1,000 then **LEFT** to 2,000 via 090....

(You can check the rest of the missed approach procedure after you've climbed clear of the field.)

Some pilots prefer to mark the numbers right on the plate with a highlighter. Other refinements are possible, too: Rounding the time from the LOM to MAP to the nearest 10, or even 15, seconds is just fine. Expecting your groundspeed to remain exactly at what you figure it to be is absurd, given the likely wind gradient you'll encounter as you descend. It's a whole lot easier to remember the time if it's a round number.

Be sure to check on the approach plate which DH or MDA you will actually use. This will depend on which components of the ILS are operating and whether yours will be a straight-in or circling landing.

Heading Downwind

Comes word from Approach: "Cherokee 266, turn right, fly heading

340, descend and maintain 2,000, vectors for the localizer."

Outside, the world is still a wall of gray, but as you turn to 340°, your ADF is pointing about 30° left. You are heading northwest and you are east of the airport. Your CDI can tell you nothing at this point, of course, for up to a certain distance, the localizer is guaranteed usable only within 35° of the final approach course, but already the ADF is telling you your relative position. The needle swings past your left wing as you pass abeam the outer marker. Your heading tells you you're flying parallel to the runway—in effect, on a downwind leg. You slow to your approach-level airspeed. Since a higher speed is, generally speaking, better than a lower one—less crosswind and wind shear effect, better control response—the approach speed will usually be based on the transition from DH to landing. Move the throttle to a setting you have predetermined will yield the target airspeed and adjust the pitch accordingly. Don't advance the prop yet, for HPN is in a noise-sensitive community that doesn't welcome the sounds of high RPM.

A word is in order here about speed. When we say 'a higher speed is better than a lower one,' we don't mean you should come screaming onto the localizer at full cruise. The controller would like you to, in order to keep traffic flowing; hence the typical "keep your speed up."

It is important to slow the airplane down to an appropriate approach speed well before the marker, especially when flying an unfamiliar approach. Slowing to approach speed is the priority. Slowing at exactly the right point in the procedure is not. It's better to fly 15 miles at approach speed than to be over the outer marker and 15 knots above gear speed. If the controller tells you to keep the speed up, just say no. You are in charge, here.

On this leg, complete the landing checklist: mixture rich, fuel system set for landing, seat and shoulder belts fastened all around; partial flaps deployed, if applicable, gear....

Gear: Now or Later?

Should you drop the gear? There are various schools of thought on this.

One, favored by the airlines, professional pilots, and many instructors, is to leave the wheels up until you intercept the glideslope, though the airplane is slowed to approach speed beforehand. Lowering the wheels at the intercept sets up a comfortable rate of descent (frequently an ideal 500 fpm) with no further power adjustment and with a fuel saving early in the approach.

However, slowing the airplane with the wheels up can demand careful manipulation and a lot of effort, particularly in a slippery airplane like a Mooney. One method is to reduce power below the approach-level setting to let the airplane slow to the proper speed, then reset it when the speed is reached: not good if you're worried about shock-cooling the engine (and who isn't?).

For the solo pilot, this technique carries the danger of forgetting deployment of the wheels altogether, as you concentrate on capturing and stabilizing the glideslope, nailing down the proper descent power setting, reporting the marker and possibly dealing with turbulence and other problems.

Outside of the macho/economy value of lowering the gear later than sooner, there is small benefit in waiting, in our opinion. What little fuel a small airplane might save, even over several approaches, is minimal compared to the damage incurred by shock-cooling your engine, not to mention the increased risk of a gear-up landing.

There are definite benefits, however, to including gear deployment in the landing checklist as you pass abeam the outer marker on the downwind leg (or as you begin the procedure turn). There is less chance of forgetting to deploy. It is easier to slow the airplane to an approach airspeed which you can establish and trim for early without need for a change later. Furthermore, consider what you would do if you had only two greens showing instead of three as you captured the glideslope: Would you really want to try to troubleshoot the gear while flying the ILS?

Lengthened or Forgotten?

As you complete the landing checklist and nail down your airspeed, scan the ADF for your position (and, at this stage, check it against the approach plate). The needle should be moving towards the tail, but if it moves to within 20° of your six o'clock, take heed; within 10° query the controller. Controllers do forget about airplanes they handle.

Normal vectoring would have you turn to base when the needle is approximately 30° off the tail. Sometimes traffic and other considerations may cause the controller to lengthen your pattern, but unless you've been so informed, a question is in order.

Somewhere between passing abeam of the LOM and the turn, the CDI should come alive if it hasn't already. Since you're headed outbound, remember that you'll have reverse sensing (unless you have an HSI, in which case you'll have a good picture of where you are relative to the localizer).

"Cherokee 266, turn left heading 280."

The approach pattern is not likely to be a squared-off rectangle like an airport traffic pattern. Rather, the "base leg" will probably be a series of vectors designed to set you up for a workable localizer intercept angle, usually about 30°.

Now your workload will build rapidly, but not disconcertingly if you're prepared for it (aren't you glad you already lowered the gear?). If necessary, glance again at your notes to make sure you've memorized the DH and the initial climb and heading of the missed approach. Double-check the inbound course, and make sure it's set on the OBS. Check that the tower frequency is set on Comm 2. Now relax and wait for the next vector, but keep an eye on the ADF. Airplanes can be forgotten on base leg, too.

In this case, no problem. The needle is just falling back to the leading edge of the wing when Approach gives you, "266, turn left heading 230."

Now you're turning to approximately 70° off the localizer course. Time to start anticipating. One more turn should put you at a 30° intercept angle. That'll be the last vector, and you can bet the controller will give you a rapid-fire clearance for the approach. And here it comes: "Piper 66266, you are now six miles from the outer marker. Turn left heading 190, cleared for the ILS Runway 16, maintain 2,000 'til established on the localizer."

It's not necessary, by the way, to read back every word, and the controller really doesn't want you to. Just the pertinent points will do: heading, altitude, and an acknowledgment of the clearance. The controller will probably hand you off to the tower immediately thereafter.

Now you have your actual approach clearance, which means that you can descend according to the published altitudes once you are established on the approach course. Without the formal clearance, even if you've been vectored to intercept the localizer and have the glideslope, you may *not* descend—you need to seek clarification.

The Reference Heading

An interesting question: As you level the wings at 190°, where are you? Had you not been told that you were six from the OM, could you know if you might intercept *inside* the marker?

The CDI is pegged to the left—no help there. DME can confirm for you that you're outside the marker, but without a clear idea of how far to the side of the localizer you are, it's tough to figure where you'll intercept it. The ADF can tell you, though. If the needle remains to the left of the nose, you'll intercept outside the OM; if it's to the right, you'll intercept inside. If it points straight ahead, you're heading straight for the marker, which is about as bad as being inside: You'll have to capture the localizer *and* the glideslope *and* stabilize your descent all at the same time.

Don't forget, here, that there are wind effects to account for: If it's blowing hard and your nose is pointing at the marker, it won't be by the time you get there. Still, it's better if you're definitely aimed to the outside.

Be aware, also, that poorly-planned vectoring may force you to intercept so close to the marker that it could be a day and a half's work to get stabilized—your first priority—and take care of whatever other tasks might be necessary. Under such circumstances, lowering the gear can easily be neglected if the wheels are still up at localizer and glideslope intercept.

The ADF is now pointing in the neighborhood of 30° left of the nose, good cause for anticipating the quickening of the CDI.

Perhaps after a slight shudder, it begins to slide from the left towards the center. At the first sign of its movement, start turning *gently* towards the localizer course and keep turning until the CDI stops. Note this particular *reference heading* on the DG, for it will stop the needle, meaning that if the needle moves to the left of center, taking up the heading *your DG now shows* will stop it and hold it—and you'll still be in the localizer ballpark. You'll have a heading from which to work to center the needle without having to guess or swoop this way and that, which is the worst, most dangerous, kind of technique.

Approaches that go sour in the last few hundred feet usually result from poor heading and pitch control. Five to ten miles out, if the rate of descent is fluctuating between zero and 1,000 feet per minute, the average rate of descent will keep the glideslope close to center.

Likewise, heading corrections of 10 or 20 degrees will keep the localizer centered, but much to the passengers' digestive distress. Even though you are weaving back and forth across the localizer, the CDI says you're doing great. This is why, outside the marker, the CDI is actually a low-priority item. Use the reference heading instead.

Golden Rule Number One

ILS golden rule number one is, *The reference heading is the heading that stops and holds the localizer needle. Though the needle may not be centered, you can fly that heading all the way to the runway and still be within the horizontal limits of the ILS glidepath.*

This is the result of the "convergence factor" discussed in the last chapter. You will be a constant number of degrees off the centerline, but you'll be getting ever closer to it in terms of distance as you fly down the glidepath funnel.

Next to two needles crossed in the doughnut, the reference heading is the best thing you've got going for you. It compensates for the wind and lets you remain parallel to the localizer. It may equal the published ILS course or it may differ due to DG precession or wind correction. If the needle is centered, the reference heading will keep it centered. (This is, in fact, basic VOR tracking—nothing mysterious, just more sensitive.)

If the needle isn't centered, make a *small* turn towards it: 5° is usually sufficient. Once the first reference heading is determined, a higher correction, say 10°, would be excessive and unnecessary. Be patient. As long as the needle is not pegged, you're in the ballpark. If it's edging towards the center as you near the runway, good. If you lose patience and determine to center the needle in one fell swoop, you'll get a swoop, and the needle may peg on the other side. A full peg means you no longer know where you are relative to the localizer, only that you're off to one side of it; you could be about to make a violent and unexpected arrival on some hillside. A fully-pegged CDI calls for a missed approach *right now.* (Don't worry about the procedure: just climb immediately for starters.)

Once you have the needle stopped and the reference heading clearly in mind, make further heading adjustments with small banks of no more than 5° to 10°.

Another technique that works quite well for small heading corrections is to use the rudder. Many pilots trained in tricycle gear airplanes are reluctant to use the rudder, preferring to make heading changes with aileron, only. This works, of course, but it's imprecise and time consuming.

If you want to make a small correction—say, less than 5°—use the rudder instead. For example, if you need 5° to the left, give it left rudder pressure. The airplane will bank some to the left (you're actually skidding, but that's not important right now). When reaching the desired heading, let up on the rudder. The airplane will be wings-level and on the desired heading. No need to anticipate the rollout, and less chance of overshooting.

Golden Rule Number Two

ILS golden rule number two is, *The ILS is not flown primarily by reference to the localizer and glideslope but with the control and performance instruments, with the scan emphasizing the AI, DG and VSI.*

When you have your reference heading from the DG, use the AI bank-angle pointer at the top of the instrument to keep the wings level *until you want to turn.* Then use the AI to keep the bank shallow and the DG to keep the heading change small, most typically 2° or 3°. Start and stop all turns by referring to the AI. Use the localizer only as a reference instrument to confirm that your change of heading is causing the needle to go the way you want and at the rate you want.

Only the AI and DG will enable you to control the airplane precisely. Fly the ILS needle primarily, and you will fly only by guesswork, chasing it back and forth. Since the needle becomes more sensitive as the airplane moves closer to the localizer transmitter antenna, this effect can only worsen.

But what if there is wing-banking turbulence or a wind change, as often happens near the ground? You'll know it quickly enough as the needle moves and your correcting turn toward the needle stops it but fails to bring it back toward the center. Whatever new heading stops the needle is the new reference heading—forget the old one. *Always fly the localizer in terms of headings, adjusting as you go.* It's infinitely easier than chasing the needle.

Golden Rule Number Three

The same principle applies to flying the glideslope, except that you must think in terms of descent rate. ILS golden rule number three is, *The reference descent rate is the descent that stops and holds the glideslope needle.*

As soon as you intercept the glideslope, begin your descent as the needle moves, don't wait to pass the outer marker. Maintain your level altitude until the needle centers and then bring back the power to what should be your previously determined approach-descent setting. Remember that you will not be adjusting the airspeed but the rate of descent to stay on the slope, so maintain your predetermined approach-descent airspeed. Remember, the rate of descent is controlled by the throttle, *not* the elevators. (Just as it is possible to make small heading corrections with the rudder, it is possible to make small rate-of-descent corrections with the elevators—but strictly limit their use. It's too easy to get into a pilot-induced-oscillation if you rely on them.)

One factor that many pilots don't pay enough attention to on approach is trim. It must be constantly adjusted throughout the approach to hold the glideslope "hands off." Failure to do this can result in an overcorrection-oscillation cycle starting.

What usually happens first is that the pilot notices a need for a correction, then initially applies elevator pressure to correct it.

Say the airplane is below the glideslope. The pilot adds back pressure to correct, but doesn't retrim. The back pressure results in a loss of airspeed, and the yoke feels heavier. When the pilot is distracted by another task, he relaxes the pressure, the nose drops and the airplane continues to descend below the glideslope. At some point, the pilot usually adds too much power and the approach is ruined; he just doesn't know it yet.

The pilot flying an ILS is faced with a dilemma. If you use constant power, you must either continually adjust the trim to hold the glideslope or keep a close eye on the AI and VSI. If you adjust power to hold the glideslope, airspeed and trim must both be adjusted to compensate. It's difficult to balance all the variables.

The rate of descent will depend on the inclination of the glideslope and your groundspeed. Check the time-and-distance tables for the rates calculated for various groundspeeds. For Runway 16 at White Plains, at a 100-knot groundspeed, the descent rate for the 3° glideslope is 538 fpm.

The wheels definitely should be down by now (check it: put your hand on the control and look at the indicators; do it again on short final), and the prop control(s) should go full-forward.

As you begin your descent along the final approach course, be guided by the five Ts:

• *Turn?*—No, except to nail the localizer.

• *Time?*—Yes, at glideslope intercept, start timing according to the figure given in the time-and-distance table for your estimated groundspeed (estimated on the basis of the wind information you got from the ATIS), in this case 2:53...call it 2:50 for simplicity.

• *Twist?*—No, that's done, and don't choose this time to set up Ground after Approach has handed you off, for you have enough to do. Besides, you'll need to raise Approach again if you miss.

• *Throttle?*—Yes, as you change the approach-descent power setting. Remember, this controls your rate of descent.

• *Talk?*—Yes, when everything else is done, report as directed to the tower. Some pilots find that talking themselves through the approach is helpful, saying out loud things like the decision height, time to go, and so forth.

Down the Chute

Now try to keep things simple. The situation is that you are flying down a chute toward a specific altitude (DH) below which you may not descend unless you have the runway or approach lights in sight. You are trying to maintain a specific heading (to hold the localizer) and a specific descent rate (to hold the glideslope) and you are fully committed to initiating a missed approach at the DH. Everything else is nonessential. It's you, the numbers, and the airplane.

There is no one to say anything to—however many people there may be aboard—except yourself, and your messages to yourself should be reports of how many feet to decision height ("700 to go...600 to go....") and your reference heading.

As much as possible, maintain an easy, light touch on the controls. Bracket the glideslope descent rate using the VSI as your primary performance instrument, just as you use the DG to bracket the heading. Your control instrument is the tachometer or the manifold pressure gauge. If there is a strong headwind, your groundspeed will be lower, calling for a smaller descent rate and consequently a higher power setting than usual. A strong tailwind will demand a lower setting than usual. Once you have the reference descent rate, leave it alone. For slight deviations of the glideslope needle, use *small* pitch changes based on the indications of the AI—don't swoop or dive after the needle.

If the GS moves by a half-scale deflection or more, recapture it using power: increase or decrease the MP by one inch or the RPM by 100, depending on your airplane. Smaller deflections can be handled with slight pitch adjustments. If you slide just a bit below the glideslope, level out and fly back into it. If you are above the glideslope by a small amount, lower the nose, but never allow the airspeed to increase or decrease by more than a knot or two. Rather, adjust the power and maintain your pitch attitude. *Diving for the glideslope is a virtual guarantee of trouble.*

While descending a little above the glideslope is acceptable, especially in turbulence, *never maintain flight below the centerline.*

Keep in close touch with the proximity of the DH and the ground by monitoring the altimeter as you call out the distances above the DH.

From the latest weather report, you should have determined at what altitude you can expect to break out. If you have a reliable copilot along, have him or her look for the lights and/or runway while you keep your scan on the panel, but make sure he or she knows what to look for and where to look. As you approach the expected break-out altitude or the DH, start to glance outside, but don't just sit there staring into the clouds. Major disorientation and even vertigo can result from fixating outside and then returning to the gauges. Similarly, try to be level when you look outside, for if you are banked when you first see the dazzling array of approach lights, they may appear to be leaning or even descending from above. If you see the lights or the runway before or at the DH, make a final check that the gear is down, deploy the flaps as needed and land—be alert for hydroplaning if the runway is drenched.

In the event that at the DH or your personal minimum altitude you don't see the runway or the approach lights, initiate the missed approach *immediately!*

Above all, don't press the regs, conditions...or your luck.

The Coupled ILS Approach

Flying precision approaches demands, well, precision. Anyone who's flown an ILS has had one of those days when it seems the glideslope just plain has a mind of its own.

Many instrument pilots have access to a nifty device that can take the pain out of flying the ILS, though: The autopilot.

Many two-and three-axis autopilots have the slightly miraculous ability to fly your approaches for you, probably smoother than you can. They're a miracle of technology.

We don't like them.

There are several reasons for this, which we'll cover in this chapter. But basically, they devolve to two objections: First, when it comes to the hard-won skill of flying a good ILS, you use it or you lose it. Second, the darned machines just aren't reliable enough to trust your life to.

Putting Your Faith in Uncle Otto

We recently asked a pilot friend if he uses his autopilot for coupled approaches.

"Sure. It's a great autopilot," he said. Or maybe he bragged. We don't know.

"Did it handle the approach better than you could have?" we asked.

"Better than me? Sure. A *lot* better than me." He was insinuating that he was rusty.

For those of you who don't have a two- or three-axis autopilot (or who may have no autopilot at all), don't feel bad. All your hands-on flying is making you a good, solid, nuts-and-bolts IFR driver. But for the record, here's a brief description: While a wing-leveler (single-axis autopilot) is limited to keeping the wings level, a full autopilot is a device which can hold altitude plus at least one more mode. The other modes might include nav tracking (following the VOR), heading hold (following the "bug" on the DG), reverse course sensing/nav, and the approach mode—including the ability to capture and hold the glideslope. There may be added abilities, such as altitude capture, rate-of-climb hold, airspeed hold, pitch hold, and more.

When you let the autopilot fly an approach for you, it's called a coupled approach: The autopilot is coupled to the localizer, glideslope, ailerons, and hopefully to the wishes and intentions of the pilot.

The "Three-Axis" Autopilot

Many autopilots which we call "three axis"—supposedly driving the ailerons, rudder and elevator—are in fact el-cheapo two-axis machines. They actually drive only the ailerons and the elevator or elevator trim.

There are also two-axis autopilots which, more or less, function in a three-axis mode: Consider that the V-tail Bonanza (among others) suffers with cross-connected ailerons and ruddervators. If the autopilot drives the ailerons, and the aileron interconnect yanks on the ruddervators, then you have what might be called a poor-man's three-axis autopilot.

Civilian training for the IFR rating lacks any kind of discipline for IFR use of the autopilot. It's pathetic, but true:

- Most training totally excludes use of the autopilot, regardless of whether one is available;
- Most competent pilots advise against flying single-pilot IFR *without* an autopilot;
- Many pilots get their commercial and instrument ratings and move right into aircraft with autopilots capable of flying everything except the takeoff and landing (including the approach), and are expected, somehow, to know the ups and downs of a machine they were never taught to use;
- In spite of this lack of training and experience, many pilots rely on the autopilot—some times right down to ILS minimums. (We know of one extreme case in which the owner and pilot of a Travel Air was so dependent on his autopilot that he used it for everything except takeoff and landing: he even had two separate autopilots installed in the airplane!)

Unfortunately, there is a logic to this sad situation. The typical CFII has a double burden: First, get the student up to the level of competent hand-flying on raw data (no help from a wing leveler). Second, make sure he or she passes the checkride, which may not include a bit of autopilot work.

So can the instructor be expected to demand an extra few hours of instruction to explain the pitfalls of the autopilot? Hardly. Anyhow, he may not know how to use it properly himself.

But now let the student graduate into the world of flight, and show him that glitzy, seductive autopilot. He soon finds that even a marginally current klutz can (and will) fly an acceptable approach with the autopilot in charge—right down to the ground. The trouble is, autopilots fail, regardless of the pilot's currency or lack thereof.

Autopilot Horror Stories

One widely held misconception about autopilots is that they're designed so that it's possible to overpower them manually no matter what they're trying to do. That's true, up to a point.

The trouble is that many autopilots don't just drive the control surfaces. They also drive the electric pitch trim motor, and that can produce forces that are beyond the pilot's ability to override.

It's widely known that one or more propjets have fallen out of the sky due to autopilot malfunctions. The theory was that the electric trim "ran away," meaning that the elevator trim motor decided to keep running until it hit the stop, and then some. The resulting force required to hold the airplane level can be in excess of what a human or two can deliver, the resulting overspeed takes the tail off the aircraft, and the rest is a matter of simple ballistics.

Because of the misconception many pilots have about how autopilots work, they don't realize that what they're actually trying to override isn't the autopilot, it's the pitch trim...until it's too late (not long: it takes a relative handful of seconds for the electric trim to run all the way in one direction or the other).

Several years ago, while preparing an article on autopilots, an editor of sister publication *Aviation Safety* did an informal experiment in a Mooney to see what kind of forces are involved in a runaway trim situation. (He did it with a highly competent instructor in the airplane, both pilots were well prepared to cut the trim motor and retrim the airplane in a big hurry, and speeds were kept fairly low to avoid overstressing.) The airplane was trimmed to a relatively slow cruise, and the electric trim was run nose-up to see how long it would take before the control forces became too much to handle. Answer: about 15 to 20 seconds.

Consider what would happen in single-pilot IFR, in turbulence, if the pitch trim ran away. You might be busy with charts and not monitoring it closely. You feel something odd (G forces), glance at the instrument panel and see the airplane climbing or diving radically. (Say, three to five seconds.) Chances are the first thing you do is grab the yoke to correct, at which point you discover that the forces are getting higher and higher. You punch the disconnect button and nothing seems to happen. (Another five seconds.) Depending on the airplane, you may already be at either stall or Vne. You frantically try to shut the autopilot off, not realizing that what you're dealing with is not really a runaway autopilot, but runaway trim. (Five to ten seconds to hit the disconnect switch again, the "off" button, and yank the circuit breaker...assuming you know where it is.) The airplane is close to, if not already, uncontrollable, and you probably still haven't figured out what's really wrong.

Based on the Mooney experiment, the editor committed the location of the pitch trim breaker to memory and began to practice emergency procedures for regaining control in the event of a runaway. These included leaning all the way across the cockpit and grabbing the right breaker by feel.

There have also been accidents associated with coupled approaches. One in particular shows how dangerous it can be to leave a machine in charge on a precision approach. In the late '80s a King Air pilot was flying a coupled approach at night. He broke out at about 400 ft agl, and punched the disconnect. No dice. He tried to shut the autopilot off using the control head. Again, no luck (remember he's almost on the ground already). He tried to overpower the autopilot, later saying he was unable to do so. By this time the autopilot had flown the airplane right onto the runway. Fortunately, there were no fatalities.

In this case the pilot probably could have pulled hard enough to overpower the autopilot, but given the short time available and the proximity of the ground its unlikely he would have been able to get the airplane under control. He could also have pulled the circuit breaker, but that, too was impractical. It's located on the far right cockpit sidewall about five feet away, amongst dozens of other identical tiny buttons. Lastly, he could have hit the master switch...thereby extinguishing all the lights at night on a low approach.

The Most Important Skill

Given that the autopilot does not think, and can make major, life-threatening errors, you'd think we'd all have it drilled into our dense little heads that the most important thing to know about Otto Pilot (aka George) is how to get rid of him. So, autopilot users: Take this Ten

Second Quiz. Name all of the methods of disabling your favorite autopilot. We've already given you a few of the answers.

Quiz Two: Can you *immediately* reach for each disconnect, without having to study labels and panel markings?

The passing score here is 100 percent, thanks to the lessons we've been exposed to with late uncouples. But in case you're new to this autopilot stuff (or experienced enough to know better), here are a few common answers. Most autopilots can be disconnected, partially or completely, in any of the following manners:

- The electric trim switch will usually take the autopilot out of the action, but will leave it turned on and ready. It's not 100 percent reliable.
- A yoke switch is normally supplied. Hitting it functions like the typical trim switch: It leaves the autopilot on, but not operating.
- The autopilot switch itself (often located on the panel or near the radio stack) should completely disable the device, along with its flight director.
- There is at least one autopilot circuit breaker. Some aircraft have several, including one for each axis control.
- The master switch.
- Depending on how your airplane is wired, the avionics master might cut the autopilot off.
- The electric trim circuit breaker will at least partially disable the ability of the autopilot to do damage.
- Most modes on the autopilot have push-on/push-off ability. In theory, you could punch all items out and disable everything.
- It is possible to override the autopilot, itself, runaway pitch trim notwithstanding. Most autopilot actuators work by wrapping a bridle cable around a drum, which is coupled to the actuator. The cable is meant to slip if enough force is applied. Alternatively, there may be a clutch mechanism in the actuator.

The Risks of the Couple

The major risk of using the autopilot for an approach is not that it is unreliable. Rather, the subtle danger is that it usually works, and builds two factors in the pilot: Confidence in the autopilot, and deteriorating skill on the approach.

Imagine yourself to be one of the sloppier, lazier pilots up there. You've spent the money, and you have a fancy autopilot, which you use for all approaches. You are a believer in the theory that machines can do this better than humans. You trick yourself into thinking that you are intelligently monitoring all aspects of the approach, something you do "better" without having to actually fly it. You're the systems manager, communications manager, and sort of general manager of the whole flight.

Something ugly is happening: You are not staying current in actually hand-flying the approach. You're relying on the airplane to fly itself.

So imagine how you react when, somewhere inside the outer marker, you get this sneaking feeling that the autopilot is taking you well below the glideslope. You've been shifting your gaze between the windscreen, HSI, and approach plate. You take your eyes off the panel now, and look at the trim wheel, which is steadily rolling forward. You've got a problem.

You hit the disconnect, somewhere near the marker. It doesn't work. And suddenly, this rusty, lazy pilot, who hasn't been flying real approaches, has to do three things: Overpower the autopilot (which includes retrimming), recover from the low glideslope position and at least recapture it (while getting ready for a missed approach, no less!), and determine whether the autopilot must be disconnected to save his rear. Of course, if it must be disconnected, he must quickly figure out how.

Do you get the picture? The pilot who becomes complacent and relies on the autopilot for the approach is the same pilot who has the most trouble if the autopilot malfunctions. in other words, the pilot who uses the autopilot on approach is slowly transformed into the pilot who needs it on the approach—and worse yet, needs it to perform properly.

On the other hand, the pilot who flies each approach by hand, and is confident and comfortable doing so, is not only proficient, he also doesn't have to monitor the autopilot, and worry that it will accidentally try to mash him onto the runway or spin him into the ground. this guy is not only better at flying the ILS (after all, he practices), he's got less at risk, because he has fewer machines to go haywire, fewer systems to monitor. While he would probably be better and quicker at recovering from an autopilot emergency than the autopilot addict, he isn't likely to run into that frightening situation. Bizarre, is it not?

An Autopilot Drill

So you think you can fly hands off, eh? With the autopilot, it's easy enough. But before you get too comfortable, think about what happens when the machine takes a coffee break. Better yet, practice for it.

While there seems to be a nasty lack of training in the use (and abuse) of the autopilot, you and a friendly instructor can correct that situation. Better yet, if you can afford it, pay the money and buy some good simulator time at Flight Safety or Simuflite.

But if you're going to do it in your airplane, consider the following exercises.

Do the exercises with a highly competent, level-headed instructor *who's intimately familiar with the airplane's systems and who has been thoroughly briefed on the exercise.* Do the exercises heads-up, VFR. When you think you have the hang of it, put on the hood and do it again. When you really think you have the hang of it, fly simulated approaches (at a safe altitude), and do it all again, losing no more than 100 feet.

If you choose to perform any of these exercises, use your head. You're about to make your airplane do things that you don't want it to do in real conditions. The forces involved can get significant, and you absolutely must be ready for them.

Remember the basics: Clearing turns and plenty of altitude, plus that instructor who knows the airplane.

• **Let the Trim Run**—Try the test we described above. Most airplanes with electric trim have only one control, on the left-hand yoke. The test works best if you're flying from the other side, so the instructor can sneak up on you, so to speak. All you really want to do, here, is get an idea of the magnitude of trim forces that your airplane is capable of generating. Try to hold altitude while the instructor dials in trim, having him monitor the indicator. Quit early. A badly out-of-trim airplane can get into an unusual attitude easily.

As soon as you feel the trim running away, disable it. Do that several times for each disabling method available, including switches and circuit breakers.

• **Down You Go**—Establish a 600 fpm descent, similar to what you'd have on the glideslope. While you hold that vertical speed, the instructor commands the autopilot to increase the rate of descent. Your job: Hold the rate of descent and fight the autopilot. Remember that some autopilots command only the elevators, while others run the pitch trim (usually the trim cuts in when the elevator servo starts to slip). *Be extremely careful of runaway trim!* Recognize it for what it is and deal with it immediately.

Do the exercise again, but with a climb command. Then do it all with the hood on. Finally, do the "disable" routines: Attempt to disable the autopilot as quickly as you identify the errors, using each method available.

• **And Off You Go**—The third game is to have the autopilot try to turn the aircraft, while you are trying to go straight. For starters, just try to hold heading while the machine tries to turn. You'll probably find it fairly easy to do (no electric trim tab to fight, only the actuator servo).

Again, try to recognize the problem and quickly disable the robot.

Then, combine the previous two exercises. While you attempt to hold a descent rate and heading, have the instructor command a turn and a climb or descent. You might find it a bit of a shock to have that yoke come back and turn at the same time.

• **Unusual Attitudes?**—In your primary instrument training, you had lots of "unusual attitude" practice. Now is a good time to try some advanced "unusuals." Have the instructor set up the unusual attitudes, then give you the aircraft as he engages the autopilot. Your job is to first regain complete control of the aircraft as you disable the possibly errant autopilot, and finally retrim for stable flight.

We warn you again: If the trim has been run to an excessive position, the aircraft may be difficult to control, and certain aircraft are impossible to control without resetting the trim. Know the aircraft, know your instructor, make sure he knows what he's doing, and *don't do anything stupid!*

Another exercise involves "bad setups." You put your head in your lap, while the instructor sets up the autopilot and describes a simulated approach. Example: "This is the back course to Runway 1 Right. When you pick your head up, you take control of the aircraft and tell me where you think we are in relation to the approach course."

That little exercise may be the most confusing—but don't let it discourage you. It involves not only a complete panel scan while you fight for control and disable the critter but also that you check the autopilot nav settings, the VOR or localizer indications, the back-course switch, etc., while trying to "think out" your position based on some sketchy information.

For revenge, put the hood on the instructor. There may be enough humble pie for both of you.

We don't want to preach, which is why we suggest you try one or more of the above exercises in your own airplane.

What Can Go Wrong?

So what do autopilots "do" to people? Sometimes, just what you asked for (if not what you wanted). Sometimes, they just go bananas. A few examples follow.

Pilot Error. If you've flown at any length with an autopilot, you've seen several "mess ups" during cruise. The most frequent are due, of course, to pilot error.

Typically, you *think* you've set the altitude capture properly. But you haven't. You shoot through your altitude, notice it at 100 above, correct it by 200 above, and bring it back down by hand. Or:

You *think* you're in the nav mode, capturing a VOR radial. But you're in the heading mode. You get busy, and you fly right through the course. You correct it by hand, and reset the autopilot.

There you have it: You can make those same two errors in any altitude mode, capturing any navaid. You can lose a few hundred feet, or get a mile off course, while flying a localizer and glideslope.

Autopilot Violence. Maybe you're comfortable with how the autopilot captures the glideslope. But one day, as the glideslope needle centers, the autopilot hesitates, and then violently pitches the aircraft nose down. You're surprised. Your passengers are surprised. Maybe there's cockpit flotsam floating in midair. It's a quirk, but it happens.

Lack of Lock-On. Many autopilots require a certain amount of time before they will lock into the approach mode. For example, the manual might state that you must be on the localizer for 20 seconds before glideslope capture is enabled. The unwary, rusty pilot might have been given a late turn with a tailwind, never suspecting that he'll capture the glideslope after he's flown well above it. The resulting pitch-down might make him think he's had a failure, leading to the "figure it out, disconnect, fly by hand, intercept from above" dilemma.

Accidental Uncouple. This is also an extremely common error. You're flying along at cruise with the autopilot coupled, and you absent-mindedly hit the trim switch to gain 50 feet or so, due to changing pressure. You forget to re-couple. You fly off course and lose a chunk of altitude. If you also lose separation from an aircraft on ATC's scope, this can be an embarrassing and financially nasty experience.

If you accidentally uncouple while on approach, and then stick your head in your lap to study the miss, you may have far worse consequences in store.

Self Uncouple. Don't forget the obvious. the autopilot can simply and catastrophically fail. Boom, it's gone. But it may not tell you anything.

Massive Malfunction. We jumped into a Cessna 210 one day, and for some odd reason thought we'd check the autopilot on the ground. When we flicked it on, the ailerons snapped to full left. We flew the airplane, autopilot off, and later mentioned it to the FBO. "Yeah, that thing's really messed up. Gotta fix that." Imagine that particular problem first showing up during a coupled approach.

Subtle Malfunction. We were out in the Malibu last week, doing some (ugh) hood work. For no reason, while flying outbound on the localizer, the flight director asked for a 30-degree left bank. In the sweat of hood work, we noticed it, wondered about it, and turned it off. When we later turned it on, it was normal. A day later, flying a cross-country, it was fine—until for no reason, a half hour into the flight it asked for that 30-degree bank. The autopilot didn't follow the command. The problem? The command bar was erratic. But what if the autopilot had responded to a similar error?

Another time, we were flying a Mooney, and put the autopilot on heading and altitude hold. We were VFR, and noticed that ever so slowly we were losing altitude, but at an increasing rate. The problem? There was a fault in the electrical system that was keeping the autopilot computer from getting enough voltage.

Information Conflict. Once, while flying a Cessna 310, the slaved flight-director gyro decided to unslave itself. We were in the soup, intercepting a localizer. If it had been coupled, would the autopilot have followed the erroneous heading? We suspect so. But because we were flying by hand, it was an obvious error and easy to spot.

External Failure. How does your autopilot respond if you're on a coupled ILS approach and the glideslope transmitter fails? Does it command the airplane to level off? To descend? To climb? Even the most rudimentary IFR training course includes the old drill, "Time it from the marker. Be ready for a glideslope failure. Be ready to fly to localizer minimums." But the autopilot didn't go to flight school, and doesn't hit the timer.

Go-Around Madness. If you want to prove how much you know about autopilots, grab a novice flier, and explain to him the different possible actions of a functioning autopilot when you hit the go-around switch.

Here are two possibilities to start with. In the aforementioned 310, the Bendix autopilot had the go-around button on the yoke. If you hit it, it would command the flight director to a normal nose-up climb position. If it were coupled, it would raise the nose for climb. Trouble is, you normally would hit the go-around at minimums while you were powered back for the descent down the glideslope. So in theory, you'd hit the go-around switch, add power, look for a positive rate, and raise the gear. Fine, but what if you mess up and don't add power in time? You're slow, dirty, close to the ground in the crud and this machine is making your nose go up. Can you say stall? The autopilot in this case is "dumb." The flight director sees nothing wrong in telling you (or the autopilot if coupled) to do something that will stall the airplane if you don't add power first.

Some autopilots are "smarter." On certain models of the Learjet, for example, the go-around buttons are located in the power-lever handles, in little recesses. The thinking is that if you want to go around, you have to add power, so make the pilot grab the power levers before he hits the go-around button or buttons (one on each power lever). But that's not all. On the Learjet in question, the autopilot will not command nose up unless one or both engines are developing at least 80 percent power, and unless the flaps are at 13 degrees or more. In other words, don't go telling the pilot or airplane to raise the nose unless you've got the power to do it. Quite a contrast to the 310's Bendix.

So, What's This Thing For, Then?

Given what can go wrong, does it make any sense for autopilots to be able to fly approaches?

Maybe. If you have a nice, heavy turbine or jet, and you have two pilots, and you're trained to CAT II standards, and have two autopilots and two flight directors, along with redundant everything and two strong bodies to overpower a malfunction, then maybe it's handy to be able to couple the approach. But why wouldn't one of the two pilots enjoy the practice and control of doing it by hand? Why not stay good at flying the airplane?

British Airways trains for hand flight on the approach. One pilot stays glued to the instruments, one stares out the window. When the window-looker gets positive visual contact with the runway, he takes the controls. Their concerns are not only with the autopilot, but with the visual transition from the panel to flying the final portion of the approach.

And now look at a single-pilot operation. Could it be that a light twin is equipped with a single autopilot, single flight director, and single slaved gyro just so the sloppy, bad-habited owner can rely on all of that non-redundant equipment and pretend to fly a professional ILS? When does this guy train? How can he be so sharp as to introduce several more items into his scan (the runaway trim light [if there is one], the trim wheel itself, the localizer and glideslope capture lights)? how can he be so confident to think that, with more to look at, more to fight with during problems and more to manage, he's safe on approach?

So what are coupled approaches good for? Maybe nothing.

Practical Uses

That's not to say that autopilots should be banned. On the contrary, they can be downright handy at reducing a pilot's workload during some of the more leisurely moments of cruise and climb. During VFR flight, they can free more of a pilot's attention for traffic scanning. They can hold a perfectly steady cruise for hours, which makes the passengers happier.

But for those approaches, we'll leave it off, thank you. A colleague summed it up perfectly once: The best way to practice for an autopilot failure during an approach is to hand-fly all approaches in the first place. The added bonus is, though you'll be able to recover from the failure, it won't ever happen.

After reading this chapter, you may disagree with us. But try out the exercises we've offered in your own airplane, and draw your own conclusions. You may agree with us that using the autopilot down low in the soup is just too scary.

Category II ILS Approaches

The ILS that most of us know and love is technically called a Cat I approach, which means the basic minimums are ceiling 200 and 1,800 feet of visibility. (Naturally, various factors can serve to raise the minimums for any given approach.)

For those skilled enough, and with the right ratings and equipment, however, there's another kind of ILS: the Cat II approach. This is an ILS of an altogether different nature, and the difference lies at the end of the approach. The basic minumums for Cat II are roughly half those for Cat I. That means that on a Cat II approach you can break out almost at the runway threshold, be unable to see the far end, and still land. Scary stuff, and hard to do.

Most of us ignore the existence of Cat II. It's intended for, and used almost exclusively by, air carriers. But that doesn't mean the pilot of a piston single is prohibited from flying Cat II. IFR *contributor Dean Gibson set out to do just that a few years ago.*

Cat II in a Bonanza

Most of us think of the airline transport rating as being the top of the heap as pilot certificates go. While the ATP is universally recognized as the ultimate pilot certificate and does require a check ride to fairly high standards, it grants no added flying privileges to the general aviation pilot. On the other hand, there's one additional privilege available to qualified instrument pilots: flying Category II ILS approaches to minimums of RVR 1200 with a decision height of 100 feet; half the minimums for the usual Cat I ILS.

If you assumed that Category II operations require a half-million dollars worth of redundant avionics flown by two grizzled airline captains, you're mostly correct. That *is* the case for airline operations. However, some years ago AOPA convinced the FAA that aircraft that have a landing-configuration stall speed (Vso) of less than 70 knots could safely fly Cat II approaches. In 1971 FARs 61.3(g) and what is now 91.193 were approved. These allow single-pilot Category II ILS operations under carefully controlled conditions.

Years ago, when I first heard of this rule change, I was excited. I've always been intrigued by what was really involved in low visibility landings, both from the skill and the avionics point of view. After all, the instrument rating is supposed to be an all-weather rating, so long as you don't fly into severe storms, icing conditions, or land below minimums. Radar or Stormscope are useful in avoiding storms, boots help in ice, and Category II (and III) ILSs extend the instrument pilot's ability to fly to lower minimums. I collected everything I could find on low-visibility operations, including a low-visibility accident report. (A Cat III ILS, by the way, can go all the way down to zero-zero conditions.)

Minimal equipment

I learned that the FAA procedures for Cat II approval require that the authorization be limited to the actual airplane(s) (not just the type or model) in which the pilot demonstrated his or her proficiency. Since I didn't own an airplane in 1971, I concluded that the utility of a Cat II authorization wouldn't be worth the effort. In 1989, after I bought a nicely equipped Bonanza, I decided to resume my 20-year pursuit of Category II privileges.

I had previously obtained a copy of FAA handbook 8440.5A (Chapter 18) which gives FAA inspectors the guidelines to use when evaluating Category II applications. Most modern IFR-equipped airplanes meet the surprisingly minimal equipment requirements. In addition to an ILS receiver, you must have a marker beacon receiver with distinctive aural and visual indications (different colored lights) for each type of marker beacon, a vertical speed indicator, heated pitot and an alternate static source. A radar altimeter is not required if you have an altimeter correction card, which you can construct yourself from the calibration data of your last IFR altimeter check.

The pilot performance standards for Cat II authorization are similar to those for an ATP. The airspeed at decision height must be within five knots of the target (for the ATP: within five knots of, but not less than, the target airspeed). The glideslope needle must remain within 50% of full scale (for the ATP: within 25% of full scale). In addition, the airplane must be "within, and tracking so as to remain within, the lateral confines of the runway extended." This means that the localizer needle must be within approximately 20% of full scale Obviously, the training for the ATP would be excellent preparation for a Category II authorization ride.

Since I already have an ATP, I just went out and practiced ILS approaches at my normal approach speed of 110 knots, which is a good stable speed for the Bonanza. It's fast enough to keep ATC happy but slow enough to lower flaps when the field is in sight. Once my skills were up to par, I submitted an "Application for Certificate of Waiver or Authorization" to the local FSDO who, interestingly enough, had never heard of FAR 91.2. (the designation for 91.193 at the time). Then I recalled the primary justification for this exception and why it applies only to category A aircraft. To quote the FAA, the requirements of flying to lower minimums in a single-pilot, light aircraft are "far less stringent...by virtue of the relatively slow approach speed and high degree of maneuverability of the small airplane."

After a brief talk with the FAA inspector assigned to my application, we agreed that an approach speed of more than 90 knots violated the intent of the exception. He further informed me that the same principle applied to IFR helicopter approaches. The helicopter's lower approach speed justifies lower visibility requirements. For example, the Astoria, Oregon ILS has minimums of a 300-foot DH and 3/4-mile visibility for airplanes (a localizer-only approach is not authorized) but the corresponding helicopter LOC approach has minimums of a 400-foot MDA and 1/4-mile visibility.

Slow speed practice

Back out I went to practice approaches at 80 knots. Since the Bonanza's stalling speed is 64 knots with flaps up (Vs1) and 53 knots with full flaps and gear down, it seemed appropriate to use 20 degrees of flaps, the maximum allowed with the Century III autopilot my Bonanza is equipped with. Use of flaps gives more of a margin above the stall, better approach stability, and better visibility due to the nose-down attitude. Also, since I wanted to be able to use the autopilot for coupled Category II approaches, I wanted to be sure that 80 knots was on the front side of the power curve. The autopilot uses the elevator for altitude corrections and it's conceivable that it could mush or stall the aircraft at slower speeds.

Although things happen a lot slower at 80 knots than at 110 knots, the Bonanza is less responsive to control inputs at the slower speeds, so I found flying the ILS slightly more difficult. I practiced a few coupled approaches and learned several things. First, you don't just engage the autopilot at the beginning of the approach and disengage it at DH. Depending on conditions, I found I had to make throttle corrections during the approach in order to keep the airspeed within five knots.

The Century III constantly makes electric trim adjustments during the approach. This can sometimes result in the airplane being out of trim at the DH. Therefore, I turn off the electric trim early in the approach, after the autopilot has made the initial trim adjustment. I found that doing a go-around with flaps and the autopilot engaged requires a little care. I dial in the amount of pitch up during the approach, and then at DH, I disengage altitude hold (the mode used during glideslope capture and descent), apply power, and turn the electric trim back on. As the autopilot retrims, I raise the gear, and then raise the flaps to ten degrees.

After the autopilot retrims further, I raise the remaining flaps. I tried raising all of the flaps immediately after applying power, but didn't particularly like the idea of climbing below Vx at a high pitch angle, on instruments, no less. It's easy to lose concentration when the autopilot is flying the airplane.This can be dangerous if you suddenly have to take control.

Checkride day

The day of the flight check arrived. I was prepared to answer questions about recognizing low-visibility clues and other matters related to Cat II approaches. FAR 61.67(d)(1)is a good study outline for this, by the way. Since the FAA handbook says that the inspector must be "satisfied that the competence of the pilot...is above average, particularly in regard to ILS approach procedures," I asked the inspector if he wanted to talk first. He said no. "Let's go fly."

We left Long Beach and I flew without the hood until the first approach to Ontario, the only field we used with a Category II runway. Then things got hectic. The weather was IMC, but breaking up due to the morning sun, which translated to some turbulence and lots of up- and downdrafts. After a manual ILS to Ontario, we did another manual ILS at Riverside, two manual ILSs to Chino, one coupled ILS to Orange County and returned for another coupled approach to Long Beach. We flew down to a 150-foot DH at each airport, followed by a missed approach. The weather had been much smoother at Orange County and I felt the autopilot had put me to shame. It's pretty hard to beat a machine with a response time of milliseconds which never gets tired. I felt like I was all over the sky on the manual approaches but the inspector said that all of my corrections were appropriate, although he thought I delayed throttle input a little. In any case, I passed the ride.

So now what? For the first year, the Category II authorization is limited to minimums of a 150-foot DH with RVR of 1600 feet. After the first year, approval may be granted for 100 feet and RVR 1200. As a practical matter, the authorization won't do me any good at my home airport, which doesn't have a Category II approach. Nearby Los Angeles International and Ontario do have Cat II approaches, so in very thick fog, they'll be better alternates than before.

I do feel that the Cat II training has given me a higher level of proficiency and understanding of low-visibility conditions. While I have some experience with RVRs of less than 3000 feet, I'm sure RVR 1600 is significantly different. The low-visibility accident report I found concerned an airplane which crashed upon entering ground fog because the flight crew suffered the illusion that the aircraft had pitched up. During the next year, I plan to find some time when Ontario is near my minimums and learn a little more about the visual clues in such conditions. One thing I already know is that there's no substitute for flying the ILS all the way to the flare.

If you think flying an ordinary garden-variety Cat I approach down to something close to minimums is tough, imagine what it's like to fly Cat IIs all day long.

That's exactly what airline pilots have to do when the weather is foul over a wide area. IFR *contributor and Part 121 pilot Kevin Garrison here gives us a glimpse into the world of advanced instrument flying as seen from the cockpit of an aging DC-9.*

Cat IIs to Minimums

Right from the start, it looked like one of those hellish days that happen once a century. The weather in Knoxville was sky obscured with a half a mile viz in fog and drizzle and that was the best we would see all day. A warm front had parked itself over the eastern half of the U.S. and it didn't look like it was going anywhere for a few days. Perfect instrument weather, if you're into that sort of thing.

We were looking down the barrel of a seven-leg day. It would be stretched over a leisurely 14 hours of duty and the weather was skuzz-o-matic everywhere we proposed to go. Our itinerary was to be: Knoxville-Atlanta-Chattanooga-Atlanta-Augusta-Atlanta-Syracuse-Rochester. Or for you identifier junkies: TYS-ATL-CHA-ATL-AUG-ATL-SYR-ROC.

I can hear the true believers sneering out there.

"Yeah, sure," you say, "you may have a long day, but at least you have a super-equipped modern transport jet to do all that heavy- duty instrument flying in."

Wrongo, dial discerners. We were flying the "start of the art," an ancient DC-9, commonly referred to around our airline as the "MD-32" or the "Cajun Clipper." You may think an airliner flying Cat II approaches has all the latest glass avionics with triple redundancy but it ain't so. We were carrying the bare minimum equipment required by the FARs to perform a CAT II operation. That's two navcoms, a coffee grinder ADF and a single radar altimeter with the indicator located below and to the right of my strawfoot knee.

To shoot an approach down to a 100-foot decision height and 1200 RVR we also have to have an autopilot that will couple on both the localizer and glideslope and a flight director that gives us left-right, uppie-downie information. The autopilot works most of the time but mainly, it's an ego booster; we *know* we can fly better than it can.

What the Rules Say

Actually, if any of you are flying your Barons down to CAT II minima and are doing it by the rules, you have my deep respect. You must be lawyers, because only ambulance chasers could keep up with all the limitations and requirements the FAA lays on you if you want to legally drop another hundred feet on an ILS.

You have to have a certificate to fly approaches to CAT II minimums. To get one, you have to fill out tons of paperwork and prove to the FAA that you can do the job without knocking over any office buildings on the final approach course. This proof includes recency of experience requirements, the minimum equipment I just discussed, plus a little book learning about such things as minimum RVRs and required cues on visual break out.

Part 91 drivers can get certified to Cat II, which was explained by Dean Gibson earlier in the chapter. It's kind of involved but airline types get lots of help. We have literally hundreds of people looking after those details for us. Our aircraft have what it takes and our training programs are set up with CAT II and III in mind. Personally, if I had to go through all that stuff to certify my Baron or Aztec I'd just stay on the ground when the weather gets that low.

Every year during recurrent, we play the CAT II game. In groundschool an op-specs guru drops by for a couple of hours and drills Jepps, minima, FARs and the like into our murky little minds. This fulfills the academic requirement for us to keep our CAT II certification.

Once we fill in the groundschool square, we move on to the simulator for our yearly scare-fest. Included with all the fires, electrical failures and windshears is one full, down to minimums CAT II approach and landing. This little simulated ride down the chute fulfills our training requirements for the year.

Of course, flying a Cat II in a box that can't kill you is much different than flying one in the real world while carrying a load of airframe ice and dealing with a full bladder. Maybe that's why so many pilots "find a home" when they become instructors in the training department.

Doing It for Real

Back in the real world of our long day, our first CAT II was the most nerve-racking because neither of us had done one in the clouds for a little more than a year. We zipped into ATL the first time with 200 feet to spare over the minimum 1200 feet RVR required. Our little automatic buddy had us breaking out about 30 yards off centerline but it was an easy recovery and nobody got hurt.

Unlike Cat I approaches where you have to see the runway in order to land legally, on CAT IIs, we're only required to see something in the "landing environment." That visual cue could be the runway end identifier lights, the centerline lights or just the plain old runway lights. We saw the approach lights off to the side and followed them into the centerline lights. No sweat. Of course, it was still daylight and we were fresh. After the first approach, we relaxed a bit, even though the weather continued to drop faster than a heavyweight in a fixed fight.

The Chattanooga turn was a piece of cake, requiring a bare minimum of deviations around thunderstorms, apologies to the passengers about how rough the air was and the usual short hold over Rome. Usually when the weather is good we don't carry much more than the minimum fuel needed for the leg plus a prudent reserve. When the weather is this bad we always carry lots of reserve. This is a comfort because of this little mathematical formula: FUEL = TIME. The more time you have, the more options you have. On a day like this, you need all the options you can get.

On almost every leg we had to play the "takeoff alternate" game, too. The takeoff alternate rule comes into play on a foggy afternoon because the DC-9 isn't certified to shoot coupled ILS approaches with an engine out. Since almost everything in multi-engine flying is predicated on losing one, the rules say that if the weather is below Cat I minimums, you have to have an alternate airport within a certain distance with weather to at least Cat I minimums. Alternate range is affected by how many engines you have left; a 727 or DC-8 has a longer takeoff alternate range than our twin-engine DC-9.

Takeoff alternates are easy, really. All you have to do is call the dispatcher on the radio and he or she will give you a legal alternate. But if you forget this little detail and the fuzz happens to be riding along expect some administrative attention from your friendly FAA representative.

Back to ATL

"Can you shoot the approach with 1400 RVR?" Atlanta approach asked during our third leg back to Hartsfield. "Ha!" we answered. Of course we could. We didn't necessarily *want* to, but we were legal, so we set up for the approach. Another aircraft missed in front of us when we turned final on the approach so our confidence wasn't all that high as we crossed the marker.

In the world of Part 121 flying, the weather has to be above minimums for the approach or you can't even shoot it. Once we're established on the final approach (glideslope intercept) we're allowed to press on no matter how low it gets. That's why we were continuing even though the guy in front of us just proved it was too low to land.

Fog is a changeable beast and by the time we got to decision height it improved enough for us to see something. The wind was calm but if it weren't we'd be limited to a 10-knot crosswind. In a visual or Cat I approach, our crosswind limit is a brisk 38 knots. On this approach, the autopilot actually found the centerline and we landed safely after seeing the runway for all of five seconds before impact.

Augusta is a CAT I airport with minimums of 2400 RVR, which is exactly what we had when we arrived back there. We shot the approach to absolute minimums and later had the pleasure of taking off with 1600 RVR (the absolute minimum for takeoff) in a rain shower.

Our third CAT II into ATL was the best because we got to carry a load of rime ice and we had 98 irate passengers who were mad because, for some reason, we were running a little behind schedule. Our times almost always go to hell on days like this because the ground controllers have to protect the ILS critical areas a little better during low weather than they do when visuals are in use.

Occasionally, you'll hear a crew on the approach frequency ask if the airport is "protected for CAT II." All that means is that the controllers are keeping airplanes out of the "sterile" area near the approach end of the runway so the glideslope signal won't be distorted by an airframe parked in the signal's groundplane. That means airplanes can't taxi up to the hold short lines so things tend to get telescoped. This is bound to slow things down.

After that final leg into ATL, we logged a successful coupled approach into the book. This is another requirement. If not enough coupled approaches are logged within a certain period of time you can't legally shoot a Cat II until you're recertified again. We flew enough Cat IIs on this one day to satisfy that requirement for quite awhile.

On into the night and our final two approaches in New York state. Nothing much happened on those legs, unless you count the low approaches onto icy runways, the fuel heat abnormal that almost made us shut down an engine and the fact that the stall warning stick shaker went off for no apparent reason on climb-out from Syracuse, scaring the snot out of both of us.

We skidded to a stop in ROC, found the motel van and laid-over. I turned on my TV and was asleep before Love Connection went to the first commercial. I probably should have gotten out of my uniform or at least let go of my flight bag and suitcase but when you're an overpaid, underworked airline pilot, it's easy to forget these things.

• Section Two •

Non-Precision Approaches

Examining the Non-Precision

In the last section we took a close look at the approach most of us fly most of the time, the ILS. There are a lot of approaches out there, however, that don't offer the benefit of a glideslope. Grouped under the collective appellation "non-precision," they comprise a menagerie of different ways to get on the ground: VOR, NDB, ASR, RNAV, LOC, back course, circling, and so on.

Regardless of the type of navaid used to base the approach on, there are several features shared by all non-precision approaches. In this section we'll take a look at generalities first, then talk in more detail about specific kinds of non-precision approaches. First up is contributor Kevin Garrison, who lends some common-sense insight into the real utility of non-precision approaches.

The Atypical Approach

What's the real difference between a precision and a non-precision approach? You may have been taught that it's the presence of a glideslope but jet drivers think of it another way. A precision approach is a normal approach, a non-precision is an emergency.

Okay, so that's an exaggeration. But for airline types, it's very unusual to shoot a serious non-precision approach more than once or twice during a month when crews fly 40 to 60 approaches. There are two reasons for this. The first is that almost all the airports that support airline service also have at least one ILS. Second, given a choice, a professional pilot will always pick the safest and most precise approach to an airport.

It would never occur to us to request a VOR or LOC just for practice. We get plenty of non-precision practice in the simulator. We're also bound by the FARs, which state that if there's an electronic glideslope available, an aircraft operating under Part 121 must either be on or above it during approach.

If you think about it, the same logic applies to the lowliest Part 91 operator tooling around in a Cherokee in IMC. Most serious IFR airports have an operating ILS so given the choice, always pick the most precise approach available when in any kind of IMC. When the weather is down, it's no time to prove what an aviation ninja you are by choosing the most difficult approach. Just as airline pilots do, you owe it to your passengers to give them the safest flight possible.

Sounds like a cop-out, doesn't it? How can you stay proficient at non-precision approaches if all you fly are full ILSs? The answer is to practice in the sim or in good weather. And never fear, just when you don't really need the practice, a non-precision approach to minimums will crop up and you'll get a chance to do your stuff.

No Vertical Guidance

Need we say here that a non-precision approach is simply one that doesn't have some sort of electronic glideslope? These include VOR, NDB, LOC, LOC-BC, ASR, LDA and SDF. Some LDAs do have glideslopes but because these generally allow only non-precision minimums, they're considered non-precision approaches.

From the approach designer's point of view, there are really only two kinds of non-precision approaches: FAFs and on-airport non-FAFs. FAF, of course, is the final approach fix and it's the point where you pull the plug and descend down to MDA. On both NOS and Jeppesen charts, the FAF is represented by the maltese cross.

Your better non-precision approaches have a FAF, fixed by DME, a cross radial, a marker beacon or facility of some kind. When the facility is on the airport—be it a VOR or NDB, there is no FAF, just a final approach point which, in it's own nebulous kind of way, is the same thing.

From the pilot's point of view, there's a definite hierarchy of exactitude in non-precision approaches. LOC-DMEs are the best, rivaling ILSs for accuracy. Next, come plain LOC and LOC-BCs, followed by LDAs and SDFs, then VOR-DMEs and VORs. For accuracy, NDBs drag up the rear. Because of this, NDBs almost always have the highest MDAs and visibility requirements.

Don't Forget the Runway

All of these approaches have some things in common, not the least of which is a runway. Most pilots miss the distinction but there's a difference between precision and non-precision runways.

A non-precision runway has the following markings: Centerline marking—paint or perhaps centerline lights; designation marking (runway number); threshold markings; fixed distance markings (on runways 4000 feet or longer used by jet aircraft) and hold short lines on taxiways.

Precision runways have all this stuff, plus various kinds of approach light systems. If you're like me, you're so happy to see any kind of approach lights when you break out that you don't care what kind they are as long as they lead to the runway.

Non-precision approach lights extend 1400 to 1500 feet from the runway while precision lights extend 2400 to 3000 feet. Are approach lights a required part of a non-precision approach? Nope. Lots of non-precision approaches don't have any approach lighting at all, although some may have REIL or more sophisticated systems associated with precision approaches to the same runway.

Where approach lights do exist on a non-precision approach, you may be given credit for lower visibility but never lower MDA. In the case of Tallahasee's NDB 36, for instance, the required visibility goes from 3/4 mile to a full mile if the ALS system is out. On the other hand, the VOR to runway 18 has the same MDA as the NDB but since there is no ALS for that runway, there's no credit for lower vis.

Getting Into the Approach

One thing that seems to go hand-in-hand with non-precision approaches are non-radar procedures. That's because non-precision approaches are often found at outlying airports and many of them lack good radar coverage. This means you may have to fly the full approach, complete with transitions and/or procedure turns.

Procedure turns are no big deal, and neither are transitions for that matter so I won't waste a lot of space reviewing them. Since there's no vertical guidance, however, you really have to be sure about when to descend out of a procedure turn to the stepdown or MDA.

On a standard procedure turn or a holding-pattern-in lieu of a procedure turn, begin your descent when you're established on the inbound course. What does established mean? Some pilots figure it's anything less than full needle deflection but if you want to play it smart, only a centered needle is on course. Anything less and you're giving away obstacle clearance.

On NDBs, plus or minus five degrees of the bearing is good enough; right on the bearing (with an accurate DG) is better. Don't forget, at an outlying airport, you may have a questionable altimeter setting plus poor runway lighting. Don't stretch the TERPS envelope any more than you have to.

Once inbound, most pilots drop down to the plate's profile view and orient themselves by finding the maltese cross. On an on-airport-no-FAF, there won't be one; just descend straight down to MDA (or a stepdown) but before you do, make damn sure you're within the distance restriction from the facility on which the approach is based. Otherwise, obstacle protection goes out the window. On both Jeppesen and NOS plates, the restriction is given in the profile view. It's usually ten miles but can be more or less.

Who's Gonna Miss?

Since there's no glideslope to worry about, there's not a lot of sense in hanging around at the procedure turn altitude once you've passed the FAF or FAP. Hustle on down to the stepdown or MDA so you can break out of the clouds in time to see the runway before you reach it. The exception might be a LOC-DME where you can set up a stable descent to the MAP. But why bother? The MDA gives you plenty of obstacle clearance so you might as well use it.

Most people say you should always plan to miss and be surprised if you see the runway. Personally, I think this is absolute bull. You should always plan to see the runway, otherwise, why are you shooting the approach in the first place?

But, just in case you don't see the runway, have at least the first course and altitude of your missed approach procedure in mind as you breeze down the final approach course. Fumbling around trying to read the missed while you're flying it is not good.

Flat-land fliers might not suffer if they botch the miss but even in a "small mountain" town like Asheville, N.C. you can run into trouble if you blow the wave off. The NDB 34 missed approach procedure requires a holding pattern around another NDB, not the one on which the approach is based. If you hadn't bothered to review the missed, you'd have your hands full if you had to go-around.

Timing Out

A non-precision missed approach point is usually determined by timing, a DME fix or station passage over a VOR or NDB. All of these are good methods, except timing, since you rarely have an accurate idea of what the wind is doing to your groundspeed. Timing is so poor a method that some pilots don't even bother with it; they simply scoot down to MDA and scram if there's no ground contact.

That's not a bad idea. On some approaches—such as the VOR-A at

Bennington, Vt.—there's high terrain off the departure end of the runway and a six-mile final approach course from the VOR to the missed approach point. At 90 knots, there are four minutes to mess up the timing.

Technically, if you start the miss following no ground contact at MDA, you're supposed to continue to the MAP. But it never hurts to start a climb immediately. Just don't turn until you reach the MAP or have otherwise assured obstacle protection.

MAPs that aren't timed—the on-airport no FAFs—can be tricky. Usually, the NDB or VOR will be right on the field, often in the middle of the runway complex. If you reach the MAP and have some ground contact, you might get suckered into trying a quick descent, a circle to land or some other stunt. Don't do it. For one, it's a violation of FAR 91.175 and for another, it's stupid.

If you time out or pass the fix, you gotta miss, no questions. I always think of a non-precision MAP as being more dangerous than the DH on an ILS. Even though DH is closer to the ground, you have a much clearer idea of where you are. Ever break out of an NDB approach with the runway 30 or more degrees off the nose? Yeah, me too. When you reach your MAP time, skeedaddle!

Think Ahead

If you use the the 5Ts, here's another mnemonic: Prior Planning Prevents Pathetically Poor Performance; the 6Ps. You can never plan too much for an approach, especially a non-precision approach. No need to make a a religion of this, though. Yes, do study the plate but don't memorize the silly thing. It won't do you any good to be staring at the plate, mouthing the words as you glide into Mt. Rockmore at Vne.

To pull off this non-precision thing successfully, here's the planning drill. First, the weather. Do you have legal weather to shoot this approach? Even though as a Part 91 operator you have every right to shoot the VOR 18 approach into Tallahassee with zero-zero vis in a thunderstorm, it won't do you much good, will it? If you have the so-called "legal" weather to shoot the approach the next question is, are you really ready for this? Are there other less demanding approaches at nearby airports with better weather? Are you trying to prove something?

Have you done this particular kind of approach before? Last month, we were assigned a DME arc, an approach I hadn't flown in 12 years. My co-pilot had done one the week before. Guess who shot the approach and who sat back and watched?

Whether you're single-pilot or crew, double check your set-up before committing to the approach. If you got bugs, use 'em. Set airspeed for 1.8 Vso or whatever you're using and altitude bugs to MDA. If you don't have bugs, keep a grease pencil handy and mark one right on the altimeter. That way, you won't have to keep moving your head down to the approach plate because you can't remember MDA. You can always rub off the mark later.

Planning should include getting all your housekeeping done early. Messing around with a nav radio inside the FAF will only foul you up. If you aren't on the approach speed you planned, your MAP time and probably the entire approach will be skewed. Do everything step by step and try to do everything the same way on every approach.

Don't Forget VDPs

On some approaches, consider a second kind of timing—to the VDP or visual descent point. Remember them? A VDP is the point on the approach where a three-degree glidepath (or thereabouts) intercepts the MDA. From that point, you should be able to descend to the runway at about same angle and rate as you would on the ILS. VDPs are depicted by a bold V that appears on the MDA track just before the MAP.

Until 1990, VDPs were regulatory under Part 91, which is to say if you were equipped to identify one, you had to use it. These days, VDP use is strictly voluntary, although the AIM does say you're not supposed to descend from MDA before reaching the VDP.

When they officially exist, VDPs are defined by DME. When there isn't one—as on the VOR 18 at Tallahassee—you can approximate a VDP by timing. Yes, timing. Just take your height above the touchdown when you reach MDA and read it as seconds and tenths of seconds. Then subtract that from your MAP time. At Tallahasee, where I seem to fly a lot of non-precision approaches, HAT is 459 feet. When rounded, that becomes 46 seconds. Assuming you're flying at 120 knots, your VDP time would be 4:21 minus 46 seconds or 3:35.

If you're using DME, you can set-up a homemade VDP by backing up one mile for every 300 feet of HAT height. At Tallahassee, that works out to about 1.5 miles from the end of the runway. To figure out where the VDP should be, add 1.5 miles to the DME data given in the profile view. Or, if you're flying away from the VOR towards the runway, as at TLH, subtract it. At TLH, the phantom VDP is at 7.2 DME.

Even when they can identify it, most pilots don't use a VDP because they don't know how to set up a normal or three-degree path to the runway. That part's easy, though. Just divide your groundspeed by two and add a zero; use that figure as your feet-per-minute descent rate to the runway. So, if the groundspeed is 75 knots, you'd descend at about 375 feet per minute.

If all this math is too much, don't sweat it; it's just fine tuning. The important thing is that if you operate into a lot of Podunk airports, you'll need to be sharp on non-precision work. That's where practice comes in. If the weather is nice and you have the time, fly a few under the hood. Then when a no-FAF VOR lies between you and terra firma, you'll be up to the task.

Non-Precision Approach Tactics

While flying the glideslope well can be a challenge, sometimes you'll find non-precision procedures that are much more difficult, due to such oddities as minimums that leave you high above the airport or final approach courses that point well away from the runway centerline.

Let's take a closer look at some individual approach procedures with an eye towards some of the features that make non-precision approaches different from ILSes, and how to prepare for them.

Planning Non-Precision Approaches

Carefully planning an instrument approach can keep you in charge of the airplane rather than vice versa. This is especially true of non-precision approaches, where a little preparation can make these approaches much more precise.

When planning a non-precision approach, the first consideration is the approach designation. For example, if a letter designator is used such as VOR-A or NDB-B, straight-in landing minima aren't authorized. This happens when the final approach course alignment is more than 30 degrees from any runway.

Occasionally, the alignment is within 30 degrees, but straight-in minima aren't authorized if the descent angle from the MDA would be steeper than a normal glide path. A good example is the VOR-A approach to Santa Monica, CA (next page) where obstacles dictate a higher than normal MDA. The descent angle from the DME step-down fix to touchdown is 4.5 degrees and the no-DME descent angle is more than nine degrees!

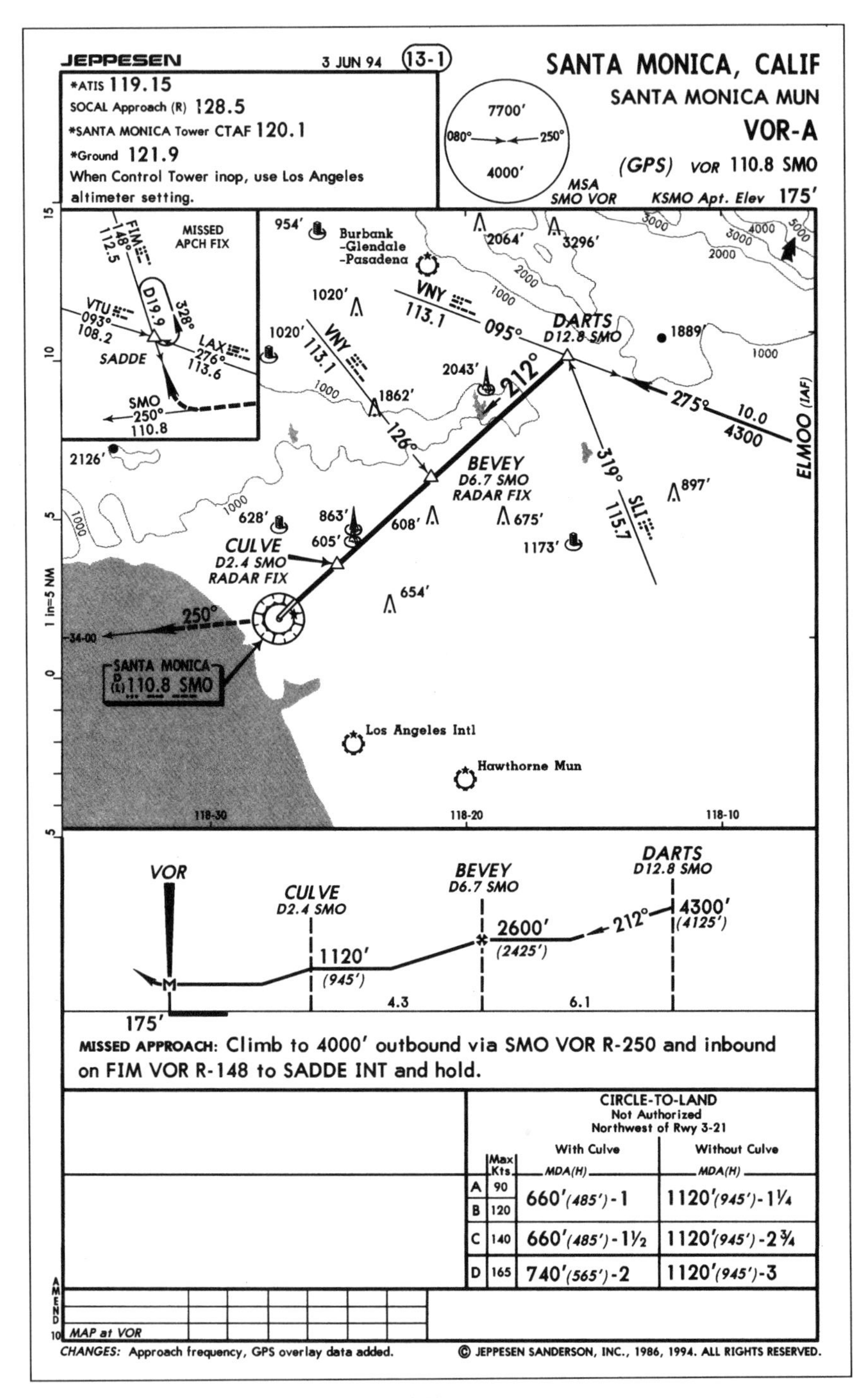

	Max Kts	With Culve MDA(H)	Without Culve MDA(H)
A	90	660'(485')-1	1120'(945')-1¼
B	120		
C	140	660'(485')-1½	1120'(945')-2¾
D	165	740'(565')-2	1120'(945')-3

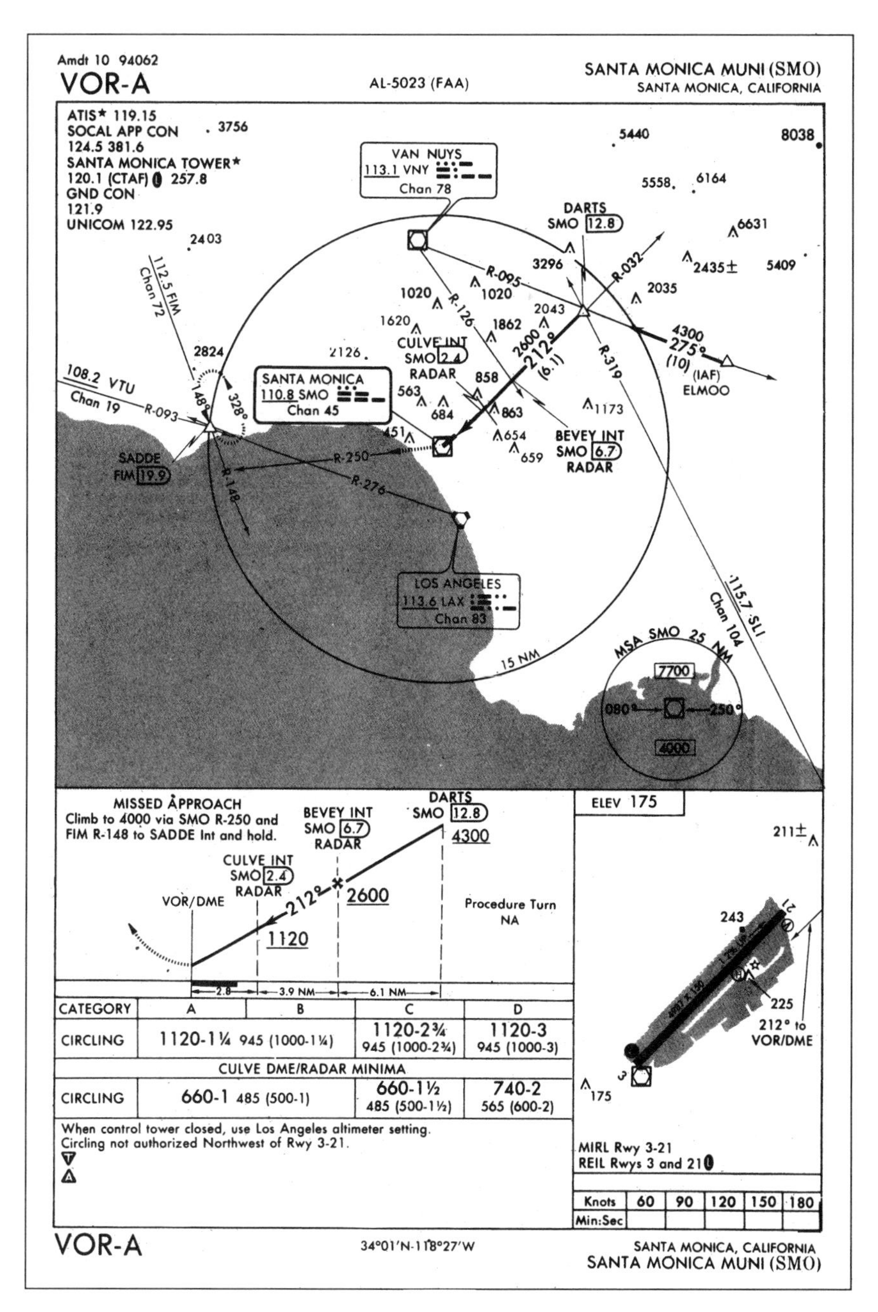

CATEGORY	A	B	C	D
CIRCLING	1120-1¼ 945 (1000-1¼)		1120-2¾ 945 (1000-2¾)	1120-3 945 (1000-3)
CULVE DME/RADAR MINIMA				
CIRCLING	660-1 485 (500-1)		660-1½ 485 (500-1½)	740-2 565 (600-2)

When control tower closed, use Los Angeles altimeter setting.
Circling not authorized Northwest of Rwy 3-21.

Knots	60	90	120	150	180
Min:Sec					

The final approach course for this approach is within 30 degrees of the runway, yet straight-in minimums aren't allowed due to obstacles along final. The non-DME descent angle would have to be nine degrees!

Since a straight-in landing isn't practical on letter-designated approaches, only circling minima are permitted. Begin planning by reviewing the chart and develop a circling strategy. The plan can be fine tuned as soon as the local winds, weather and landing runway is determined. Even though winds might vary by the time you arrive, have a strategy in mind.

Planning to maneuver

There are no required patterns for circling maneuvers. You could fly across the runway and turn left or right to a downwind or fly along the runway centerline and then turn downwind in either direction. Whichever you chose, keep in mind that circling minima are based on a clearance of 300 feet or more from any obstructions within a fixed radius of the runway threshold. At speeds below 120 knots this radius is 1.5 miles (1.3 miles at speeds below 90 knots).

In addition to obstructions, remember that other aircraft can legally operate VFR clear of clouds with 1 mile visibility in uncontrolled airspace. Someone could be doing touch and goes, traffic patrol or crop dusting. Avoid the mind-set that no one else would be crazy enough to be there.

Planning a circling maneuver and a possible missed approach requires good visualization. Circling at 500 feet above an airport with one mile visibility can lead to disorientation.

Visualizing the pattern

One way to develop an action plan is to mentally place yourself on the final approach course and develop an image of the anticipated runway pattern. For visual orientation, NOS charts depict the final approach course alignment with an arrow on the airport diagram. Jeppesen runway diagrams are on a separate page and do not show course alignment. To create the best mental picture with Jeppesen charts, place a pencil over the final approach course. Then, slide the airport diagram directly underneath the pencil and imagine flying along the pencil line.

If visual contact is lost at any stage during the circling maneuver, execute a missed approach immediately. This is easier said than done. Once you've maneuvered toward the landing runway and then lost sight of the airport, you'll probably be satisfied just to know which direction is up let alone where to go for the missed approach. Integrating the missed approach procedure into the circling plan is vital. When entering the scud at 500 feet, concentrate on flying the airplane, not checking the chart. Anytime you're in doubt about the missed approach, turn toward the runway to remain in the circling protected area.

Here is one way to plan both the circling maneuver and the missed approach procedure at the same time. At Key West, FL for example (see charts on pp 72-73), the VOR-B approach brings you in from the northwest toward an east-west runway. Since the missed approach requires a right turn to the south and back to the VOR, you could make all turns to the right. Position for a right downwind to Runway 27, if possible, or fly over the airport and enter a right downwind for Runway 9. If you lose sight of the airport at any point, turn right again and proceed to the VOR. However unsettling the lapse into IMC, you'd only need to remember to make a climbing right turn to the VOR.

Decision points

On a non-precision approach, straight-in landing minima apply and a straight-in landing is possible if you're visual with the runway in sufficient time. However, there is a pitfall on such an approach. Your mind-set is to land straight ahead and not to circle. As time ticks by, the adrenaline surges. If the runway doesn't come into view until the last second, your mind will shout LAND! and you'll commence a dirty dive for the numbers. The action is dangerous at best.

To avoid the dirty dive, the high-speed float and the chance of sliding off a short or rain-slicked runway, create your own land-or-circle decision point. The steepest descent angle from the MDA you'd probably be comfortable making in low visibility conditions would be four degrees or 400 feet per mile. If the MDA is 600 feet agl, your straight-in landing decision point should be 1.5 miles from touchdown. At 120 knots groundspeed, this is 45 seconds. If the MDA is higher, the decision point should be one to one and a half minutes from the MAP, depending on groundspeed.

You can compute each situation independently, but it's easier to work in round numbers. On average for most light singles and twins, the one minute point works well. If your groundspeed is closer to 90 knots or the MDA is 800-900 feet agl, use 1.5 minutes. Subtract this time from the inbound procedure time and you have your land or circle decision point.

For example, assume the inbound time from the final approach fix is 2:58. As you cross the final approach fix, begin timing and descend promptly to the MDA. If the runway isn't visible as the timer reaches 1:58, shift to plan B: circle to land. If the runway suddenly appears, you're committed to your circling strategy. If you don't see the runway as the timer reaches 2:58, execute a missed approach.

This technique depends on a timed approach with the MAP at the runway threshold. Many VOR and NDB approaches have an MAP at

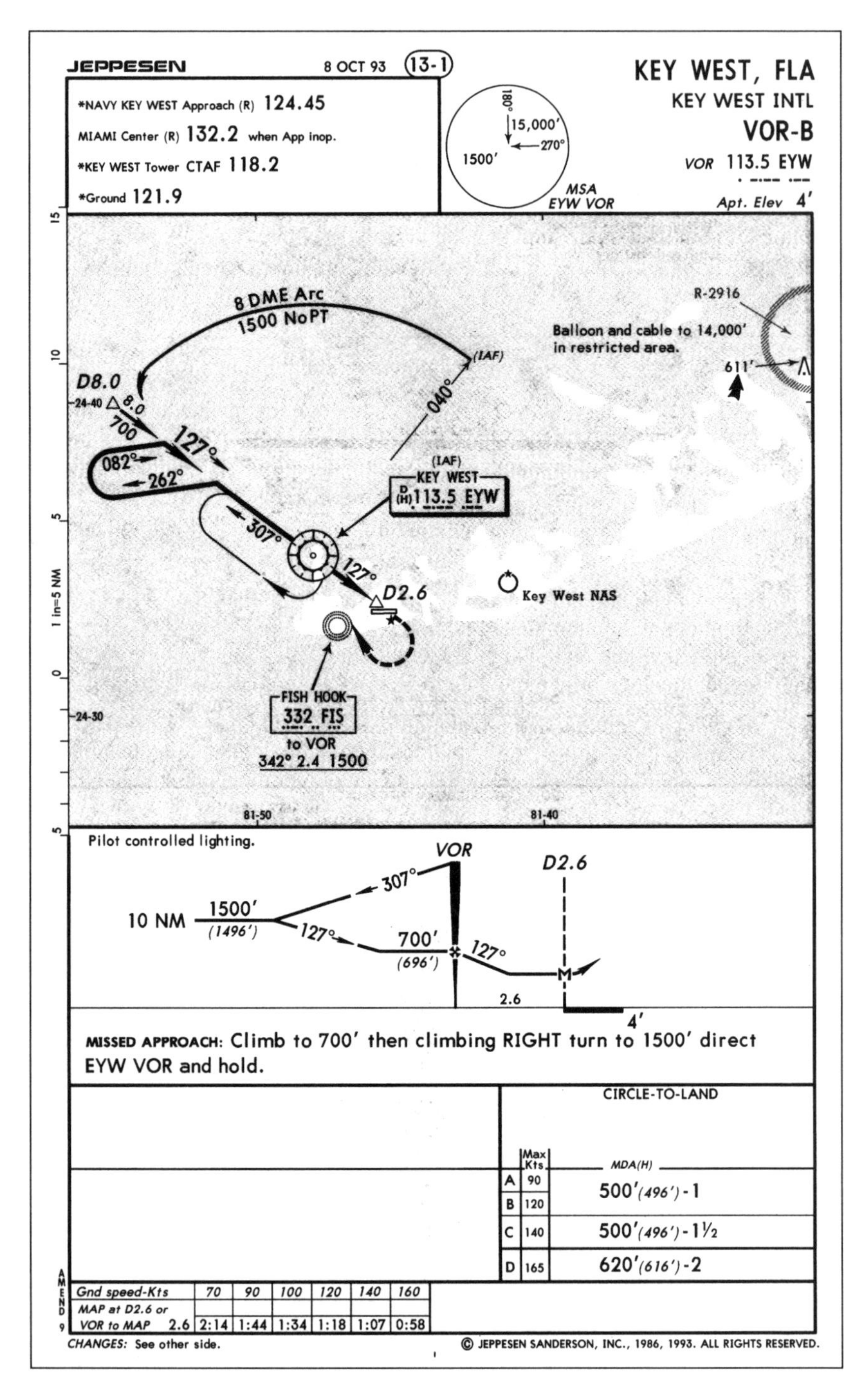
JEPPESEN
8 OCT 93
13-1
KEY WEST, FLA
KEY WEST INTL
VOR-B
VOR 113.5 EYW
Apt. Elev 4'
*NAVY KEY WEST Approach (R) 124.45
MIAMI Center (R) 132.2 when App inop.
*KEY WEST Tower CTAF 118.2
*Ground 121.9
180°
15,000'
270°
1500'
MSA
EYW VOR
8 DME Arc
1500 NoPT
(IAF)
040°
D8.0
8.0
700
127°
082°
262°
307°
(IAF)
KEY WEST
113.5 EYW
127°
D2.6
Key West NAS
R-2916
Balloon and cable to 14,000' in restricted area.
611'
FISH HOOK
332 FIS
to VOR
342° 2.4 1500
24-40
24-30
81-50
81-40
1 in=5 NM
Pilot controlled lighting.
VOR
D2.6
10 NM
1500'
(1496')
307°
127°
700'
(696')
127°
2.6
4'
MISSED APPROACH: Climb to 700' then climbing RIGHT turn to 1500' direct EYW VOR and hold.
CIRCLE-TO-LAND
Max Kts
MDA(H)
A 90
B 120
500'(496')-1
C 140
500'(496')-1½
D 165
620'(616')-2
Gnd speed-Kts 70 90 100 120 140 160
MAP at D2.6 or VOR to MAP 2.6 2:14 1:44 1:34 1:18 1:07 0:58
AMEND 9
CHANGES: See other side.
© JEPPESEN SANDERSON, INC., 1986, 1993. ALL RIGHTS RESERVED.

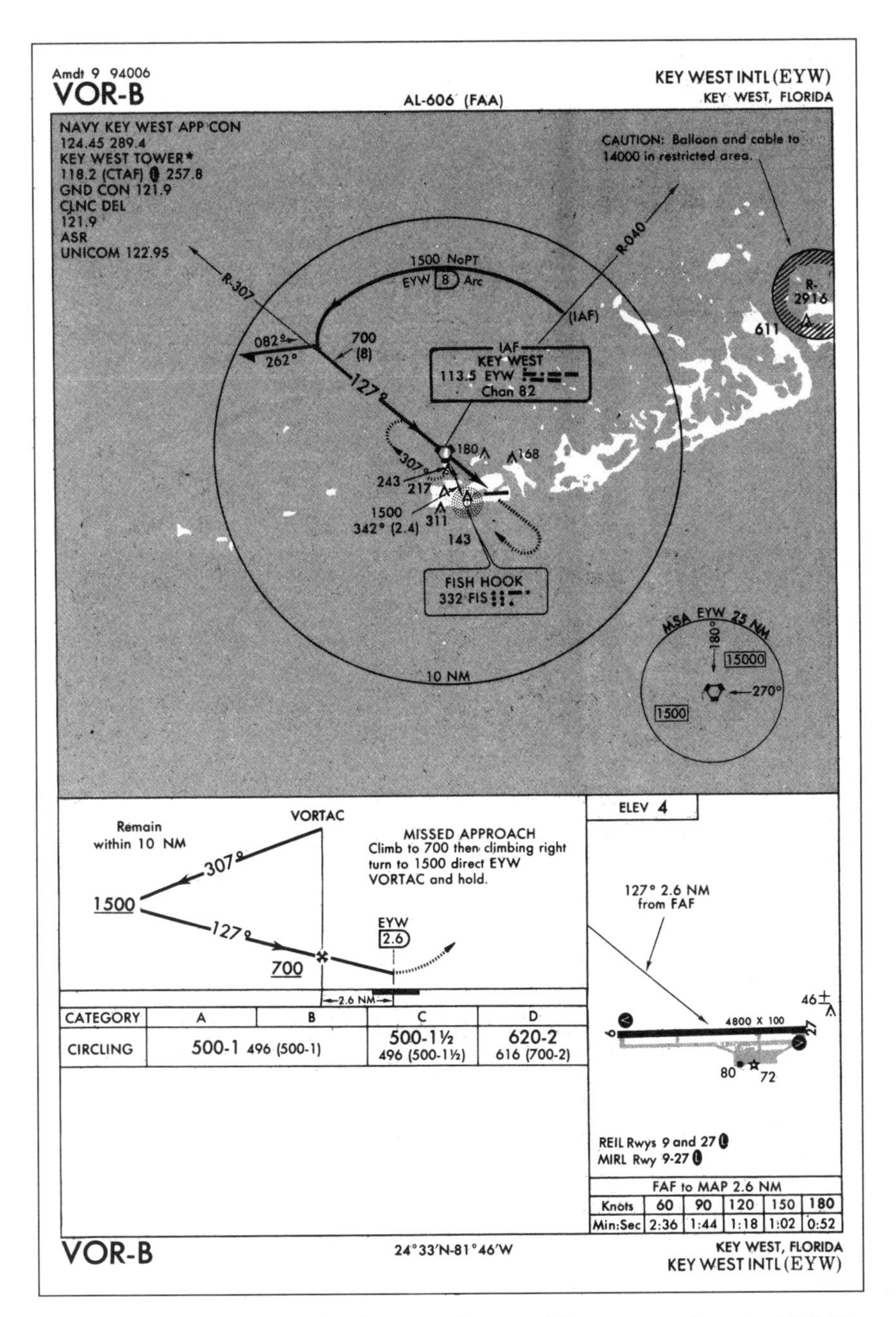

CATEGORY	A	B	C	D
CIRCLING	500-1 496 (500-1)		500-1½ 496 (500-1½)	620-2 616 (700-2)

FAF to MAP 2.6 NM					
Knots	60	90	120	150	180
Min:Sec	2:36	1:44	1:18	1:02	0:52

The final approach course for this procedure positions you at almost mid-field. Circling to Rwy 9, you can pass over the runway to a right downwind. Circling for 27, you're positioned for a right downwind entry.

the VOR or NDB, which is centered on the airfield. In this situation add another 20 seconds in your computations. If the MAP is based on DME, base your decision on distance.

Circling minima are almost always higher than their straight-in counterparts. Once you're beyond your landing decision point, you might have to climb to execute the circling approach. If the cloud base precludes a climb, commit to the missed approach. If the runway comes into view later, don't be suckered into the dirty dive. Go for the missed approach and buy some thinking time.

Where to look

While early visualization of the runway view is vital for a circling procedure, it's also important for a straight-in landing. For example, you're set up for the VOR Runway 9 approach to Tampa, FL (charts pp 75-76) . Although the chart indicates straight-in approach minima, the inbound course is 063.

Your straight-in landing decision point is 4:30. Suppose you look up ahead and see only the ground below; no runway, no approach lights, just haze. The runway is well to the left of the nose, but our mind set when tracking perfectly is to see the runway directly ahead. Even with better runway/approach alignment, drift correction can have considerable impact on the runway view in the wind screen.

Also remember that NDB signals become increasingly inaccurate with distance. Since you are generally tracking away from the beacon on final approach, consider that the runway could be right or left of the nose despite perfect tracking. If you imagine where the runway view is likely to be at an early stage, your chances for a straight-in landing will improve.

Check it twice

There are two other important items to consider on any approach. Since you'll be descending to as little as 200 feet above the surface, check your altimeter at least twice. Immediately set it when you receive the ATIS and check it again as you begin the approach. A difference of 50-100 feet could make the difference in completing the approach safely or not completing it at all. Be particularly careful at night and in turbulence. ILS approaches have a glideslope crossing altitude at the final approach fix (a very sensible cross-check), but no such check is available for non-precision approaches.

Also consider the source of the altimeter setting. Often approach minima change depending on whether the setting is a local one or one from a more distant airfield.

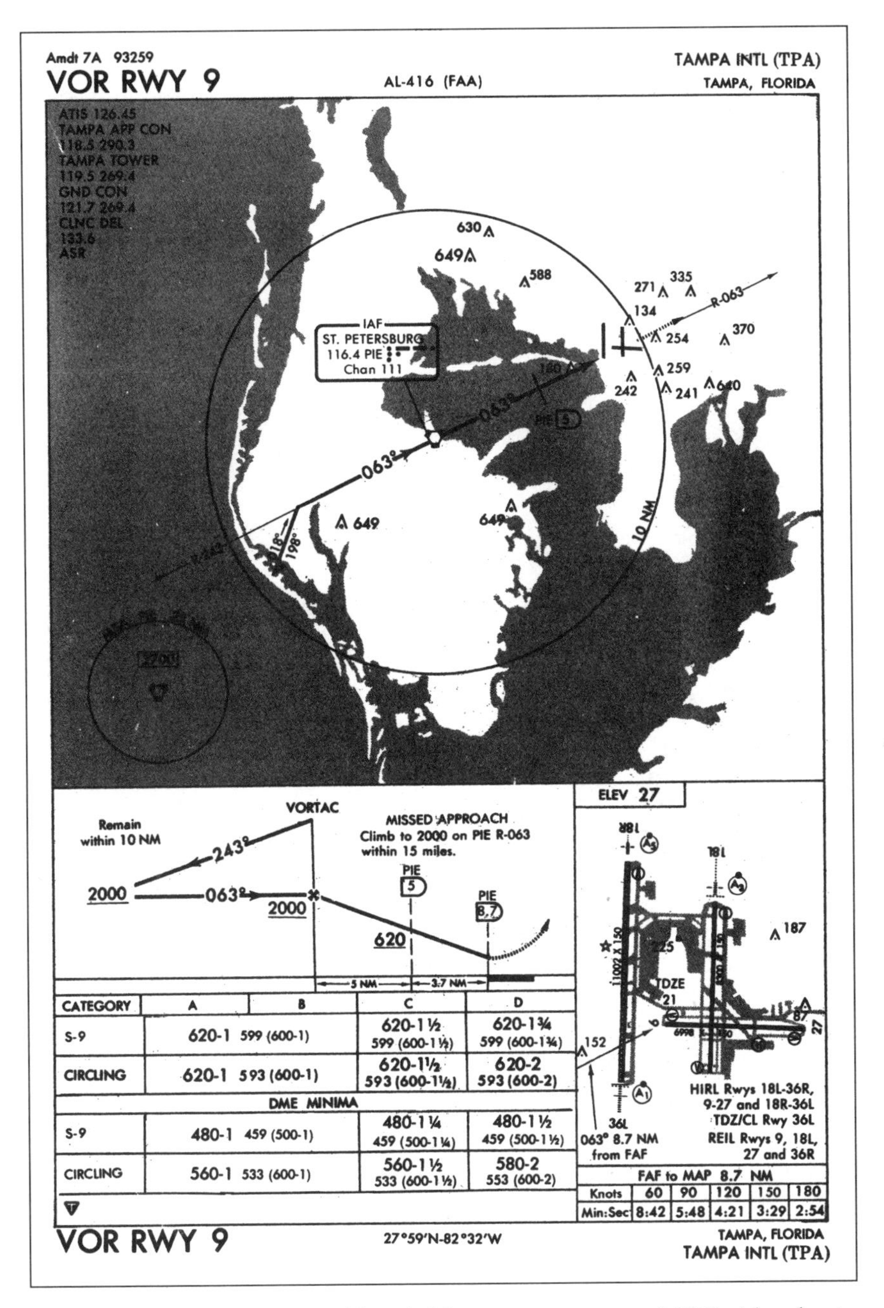

If your VOR is accurate, you'd probably assume a centered CDI at breakout. Not so: The final approach course is offset 27 degrees, which would place the runway well to the right of the nose.

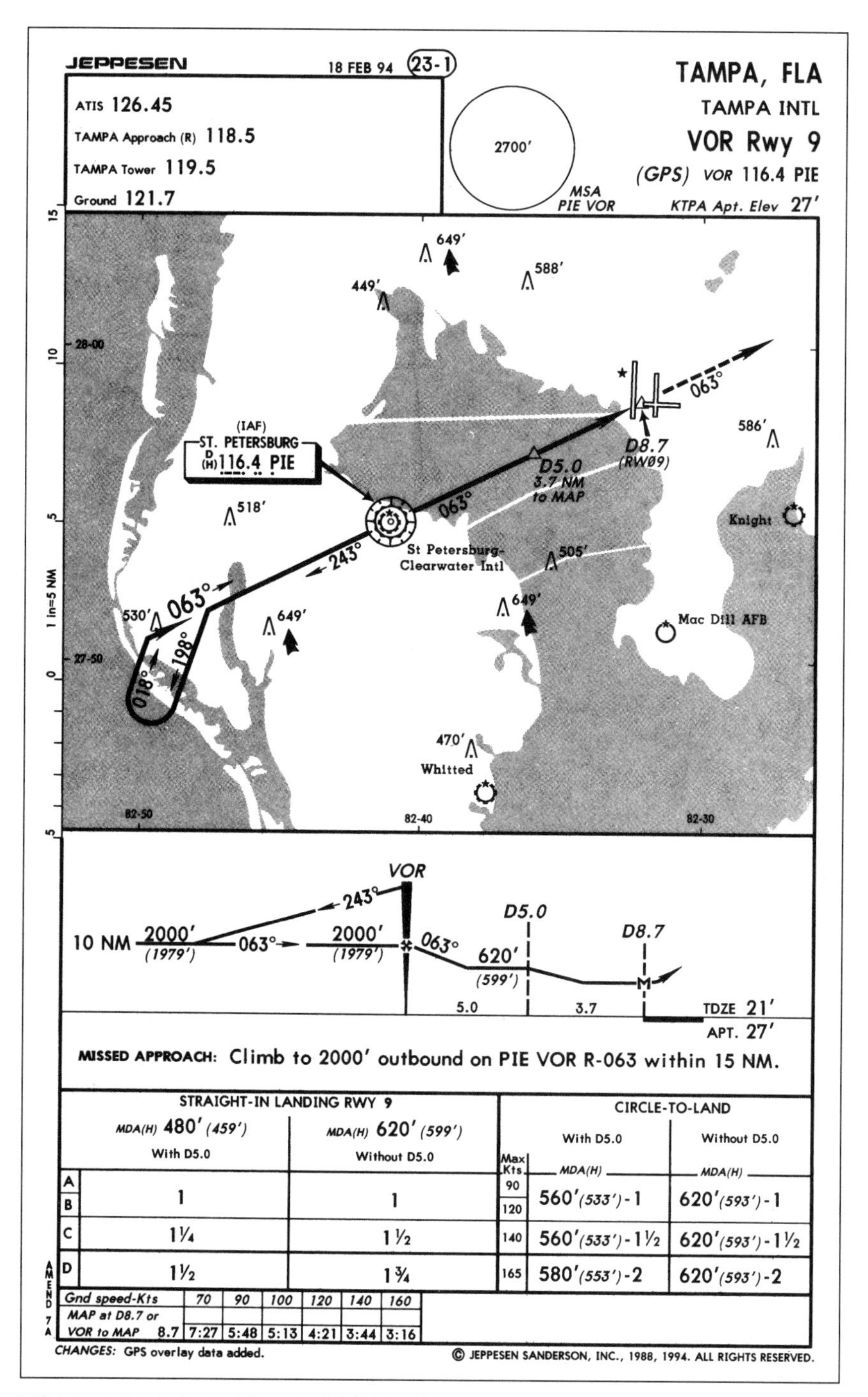
JEPPESEN
18 FEB 94
23-1
TAMPA, FLA
TAMPA INTL
VOR Rwy 9
(GPS) VOR 116.4 PIE
ATIS 126.45
TAMPA Approach (R) 118.5
TAMPA Tower 119.5
Ground 121.7
2700'
MSA PIE VOR
KTPA Apt. Elev 27'
649'
588'
449'
28-00
(IAF)
ST. PETERSBURG
D (H) 116.4 PIE
063°
586'
D8.7 (RW09)
D5.0
3.7 NM to MAP
518'
Knight
St Petersburg-Clearwater Intl
243°
505'
063°
530'
649'
649'
Mac Dill AFB
198°
018°
27-50
470'
Whitted
82-50
82-40
82-30
1 in=5 NM
VOR
243°
D5.0
D8.7
10 NM
2000' (1979')
063°
2000' (1979')
063°
620' (599')
5.0
3.7
TDZE 21'
APT. 27'
MISSED APPROACH: Climb to 2000' outbound on PIE VOR R-063 within 15 NM.
STRAIGHT-IN LANDING RWY 9
MDA(H) 480' (459') With D5.0
MDA(H) 620' (599') Without D5.0
CIRCLE-TO-LAND
With D5.0
Without D5.0
Max Kts
MDA(H)
A B: 1 | 1 | 90 120 | 560'(533')-1 | 620'(593')-1
C: 1¼ | 1½ | 140 | 560'(533')-1½ | 620'(593')-1½
D: 1½ | 1¾ | 165 | 580'(553')-2 | 620'(593')-2
Gnd speed-Kts 70 90 100 120 140 160
MAP at D8.7 or VOR to MAP 8.7 7:27 5:48 5:13 4:21 3:44 3:16
AMEND 7A
CHANGES: GPS overlay data added.
© JEPPESEN SANDERSON, INC., 1988, 1994. ALL RIGHTS RESERVED.

The other vital instrument double-check is the heading indicator (HI). Once you've leveled on the inbound course, check the HI and check it once again when reaching MDA. On an NDB approach, it might appear that you're accurately tracking from the beacon, but you could be on the wrong track due to an errant gyro. If the inbound leg is a long one, you could be well out of bounds when your timing is complete.

Apply the strategy

Preparation can turn a would-be nightmare into a satisfying experience. On non-precision approaches, have a scheme in mind for circling and missed approaches. Visualize the entire runway picture, not just a strip of concrete straight ahead since the chances are on a non-precision approach that the runway will be anything other than on the nose. Once on final, complete the aircraft checks and focus on your decision criteria: MDA, straight-in landing point, circling minima and approach time. At the MAP or any point during the circling maneuver if visual contact is lost, immediately apply your missed approach strategy.

If the weather is well above minimums and the approach is merely a cloud-break procedure, develop your full plan anyway. The practice will be invaluable and on the occasion when you have to fly the entire approach to bare-bones minima you'll do so with confidence.

We feel that the terms "precision" and "non-precision" as they are applied to approaches are really misnomers. The so-called "precision" approach is actually much easier to fly and requires less of the pilot than a "non-precision" approach.

Many pilots fly non-precision approaches in a sort of sloppy, rule-of-thumb manner that can leave them at certain points on the approach uncertain of where they actually are.

But there are ways to add precision to your non-precision approaches. Here are some tips.

Non-Precision Precision

The dictionary defines precision as the quality or state of being precise or exact. The FAA defines instrument approaches as either precision or non-precision. At the risk of being semantically nitpicking, we take exception to this. An approach without a glideslope should be flown with as much if not more precision than an approach with a glideslope. The term non-precision approach suggests that the pilot does not have to be exact or precise. The facts simply do not support this; more accidents occur during non-precision approaches than during precision approaches.

Flying down a glideslope with the needles centered does require precise flying, make no mistake. But looked at on a larger scale, an ILS approach does not require the precision of a VOR or ADF approach, since the pilot has more information available. For example, if you do not maintain a proper descent rate during an ILS approach, the glideslope immediately indicates how much correction is needed. During a VOR approach, if you suddenly realize that you have not maintained a proper descent rate, there are no indications of how far off you are, or what the proper descent rate should be. You can only guesstimate.

Almost every ILS approach requires approximately the same rate of descent to maintain the glideslope for a specific approach speed. This is not the case for VOR and ADF approaches.The same holds true for course information. Once inside the final approach fix of an ILS, a specific needle deflection on the localizer usually requires the same heading change to recenter it. The same method cannot always be applied to VOR and ADF approaches due to the varying distances from the navigational facility used for the approach.

More Precision Needed

Since course guidance is not as accurate during a non-precision approach, the pilot must fly with more precision. The FAA flight test standards for a VOR approach only require that the needle not be fully deflected. Depending on your distance from the facility and the accuracy of the VOR receiver, a full-scale needle indication could place you out of protected airspace.

Also, the standard of not more than a 10° course deviation during an ADF approach could place you out of protected airspace as a result of compass errors. With these possible errors, extra precision is required by the pilot.

How do we obtain that precision? Course guidance is fairly simple. At ten miles from a VOR, a three-dot deflection on the CDI is 6° or one mile. This will keep you in protected airspace even with a four-degree error on the VOR. As the distance from the VOR increases, the width of protected airspace also increases, so a three-dot deflection will keep you safe. Anything more than that could be dangerous depending on the accuracy of your receiver.

Allowing no more than a three-dot deflection will also keep your heading changes to less than 10° when recentering the needle. A four- or five-dot deflection eight miles from the VOR could require a sizable intercept heading. The same guideline applies to NDB approaches. Try to remain within 6° of the final approach course. Naturally, an NDB course cannot always be tracked this accurately, but do your best. Never exceed 10° off course.

Planning Descent Rate

Now let's discuss a precision descent during a non-precision approach. The key is planning the proper descent rate and flying the vertical speed indicator (VSI) much the same as a glideslope. Ask a group of instrument pilots the descent rate they use for an NDB or VOR approach and you will hear one of two answers; get down as fast as possible, or maintain 500-600 feet per minute. Neither answer is correct.

The first does not involve any precision. Just getting down as fast as possible doesn't offer you any reference for the descent. If you have a specific descent rate in mind, you'll be smoother, more in control, and therefore safer during the let-down. Plus, your passengers won't think they're on the Cyclone at Coney Island when you initiate the descent, diving hell-for-leather for the MDA.

So why not use the 500-600 fpm target as a rule of thumb? Sometimes it will actually work out, but in many cases it simply won't get you down fast enough.

Let's say you're on a typical NDB approach. The NDB is located 3.9 miles off the airport and the missed approach point is at the runway threshold. The altitude for passing the final approach fix is 1700 feet and the minimum descent altitude is 900 feet. Based on an approach speed of 90 knots, you determine that the time to the missed approach point is two minutes and thrity-six seconds. (Don't worry about the math...the time is printed on the chart for you.) What minimum rate of descent is needed?

If your answer is slightly more than 300 fpm based on losing 800 feet in two minutes and thirty-six seconds, your answer is not correct. Doing so will place you *at the runway threshold* and the MAP at an altitude of 556 feet agl. How do you expect to make a safe landing from this position? For that matter, if you break out at MDA and already over the runway, there's even a good chance you won't be able to see anything out the windshield but the trees at the far end of the airport, since you're practically at pattern altitude.

Arrive Early at MDA

Obviously, it's a good idea to reach the MDA prior to the missed approach point. The generally accepted rule is to arrive at the MDA the same distance from the missed approach point as the visibility minimum. For example, if the visibility minimum is one mile, you should be at the MDA at least one mile before the MAP. The math required to calculate that distance can be difficult.

Try this method instead: Plan to arrive at the MDA at least one minute before the MAP. This gives you ample time to look for the runway and configure the aircraft for landing. To use the previous example, you should plan to reach the MDA in one minute and thrity-six seconds instead of three minutes and thirty-six seconds, so the descent rate should be approximately 600 fpm. Although this descent rate may not appear excessive, there are many other non-precision approaches that require a steeper descent rate in order to see the runway before the missed approach point.

Determining the proper descent rate is the first step to a precise non-precision approach. Once you have determined the time to MAP, subtract one minute and divide the remainder into the altitude to be lost. You don't have to be exact. For example, if the time to MAP is two minutes and forty seconds, with 1200 feet to descend, round off your descent rate to 800 fpm. It is important to calculate that descent rate: It gives you a target to hit, a guideline by which you can fly the approach.

Once you know the descent rate needed to arrive at the MDA one minute prior to the missed approach point, a precision approach can be accomplished. In the previous example, use the 800 fpm on the VSI as the center of a glideslope. If your rate of descent increases to 1000 fpm, raise the pitch slightly (and/or adjust power, as described in the last section). Conversely, a 600 fpm rate of descent means you need to lower the pitch slightly. Now you are flying a precision approach by using the VSI as a glideslope.

There are two advantages to this method. First, although your airspeed may vary, it should average the airspeed required to maintain the required rate of descent. The second advantage is that if you become confused while timing the approach, you should be approximately one minute from the MAP when leveling at the MDA. If you just let down as fast as possible after the fix, when you hit MDA you really don't know how far from the MAP you are. Your speed will probably have been higher than average during the descent, so your time calculation will be off.

This technique can also be applied when flying a non-precision approach where the navigational facility is on the airport and the procedure does not have a final approach fix. In this case, if you normally fly outbound for two minutes at normal approach speed, plan the descent for two minutes. The time required to complete the procedure turn will provide the additional minute needed to arrive at the

MDA. Any wind component moving from the airport towards you will add a bit of a safety cushion, but if you're making the approach with a tailwind you should allow for it. Be conservative.

Keep it Precise

This is one technique for flying non-precision approaches with precision. During a VOR approach, never allow more than a three-dot deflection of the CDI. In the case of an NDB approach, attempt to remain within six degrees. Always program a descent rate to arrive at the MDA at least one minute prior to the MAP and then fly the VSI at that descent rate like a glideslope. Try these techniques and you'll be surprised how smoothly you fly the next non-precision approach.

The NDB Approach

Fortunately, few of us really need to fly NDB approaches in actual conditions. That's a good thing, because making an NDB approach to minimums in actual conditions is one of the toughest things an IFR pilot has to do.

It's counterintuitive, the radios are imprecise, and to further complicate matters the darned indicator might be located on the far side of the cockpit.

But it's not impossible. Here's a look at how best to handle the NDB approach (hint: positional awareness is a big factor), with a detailed examination of two approaches.

The Lost Art of the NDB

Does the thought of NDB holding and an approach to circling minimums in a mountainous area without radar send chills up and down your spine? It needn't if you're proficient at tracking the needle and maintaining positional awareness.

We'll discuss two challenging NDB approaches, but first we'll do a quick review of determining relative bearing, tracking and intercepting magnetic bearings.

Relative Bearing

The *Instrument Flying Handbook* defines relative bearing as the bearing line measured clockwise from the nose of the aircraft. On a fixed-card ADF, the relative bearing is simply whatever the needle points to. For example, if the ADF needle indicates 220, the relative bearing is 220°.

To figure the magnetic bearing to the station, add the relative bearing to your heading. Subtract 360 if the total is over 360 and that will be your magnetic bearing to the station. For example, your relative bearing is 220 and your magnetic heading is 160. Your bearing to the station would be 160 + 220 = 380 - 360 = 20°. Your bearing from the station would be the reciprocal or 200°.

If you don't feel comfortable with this, spend some time using pencil and paper to simulate various aircraft positions and figuring bearings to and from the station. In the previous example, you wouldn't want ATC to think you were on the 20-degree magnetic bearing from the station.

Tracking

Tracking is flying a straight line to or from a station while correcting for drift along the way. You must be proficient at tracking since there are NDB approaches with nearby obstructions that could impact on your longevity if not properly flown.

Tracking to the station:

1. Fly a heading that puts the head of the ADF needle on the nose of the aircraft.
2. If the head of the needle moves to the left of the nose, the wind is from the left and your track is to the left. If it moves to the right of the nose, the wind is from the right and your track is to the right.
3. Wait until the needle points at least 5 degrees to either side of the nose, then turn toward the head of the needle double the number of degrees of deflection. For example, if the needle points 10 degrees left of the nose, turn 20 degrees left.
4. Hold this new heading until the needle is deflected the same number of degrees from the nose as the amount of correction. When this happens, turn back to your desired track and apply some drift correction. Using our previous example, when the needle is 20 degrees off the nose, turn 10 degrees toward the desired track and leave ten degrees as drift correction.
5. Hold the new heading until the needle moves in either direction. When this happens, it indicates that your drift correction was too small or too large and you must make an adjustment.

Tracking from the station:

The procedure is the same for tracking from the station as it is to the station except that you work the deflections from the tail when tracking from the station.

1. Fly a heading that puts the head of the needle on the tail.
2. If the head of the needle moves to the right of the tail, the wind is

from the right and your track is to the right. If the needle moves to the left of the tail, the wind is from the left and your track is to the left.

3. Wait until the needle is at least 5 degrees to either side of the tail, then turn toward the head of the needle double the number of degrees of deflection.

4. Hold this new heading until the needle is deflected the same number of degrees from the tail as the amount of correction. When this occurs, turn back to your desired track and apply a small drift correction.

5. Hold the new heading until the needle moves in either direction. When this happens, it indicates that your drift correction was too small or too large and you must make an adjustment.

Intercepting magnetic bearings:

1. Turn to the heading of the magnetic bearing you want to intercept. This parallels the track that you'll intercept. Concentrate on holding the heading to within a few degrees.

2. Turn toward the head of the needle double the number of degrees it's deflected from the nose, but not more than 90 degrees.

3. Hold this heading until the needle is deflected the same number of degrees as your present heading is to the desired heading (track). The elapsed time for this to take place will be your time to the station. What you've done is constructed an Isosceles triangle and solved a simple time and distance problem.

4. Turn to the desired magnetic bearing and correct for drift as previously described.

The same procedure for intercepting predetermined outbound tracks is the same as inbound interceptions except you use the tail of the aircraft as the reference point.

The NDB Approach

Now let's review two interesting NDB approaches. Refer to the NDB Runway 16R for Reno, NV (next page). There are four transition routes to Sparks NDB, the only IAF authorized for this procedure. Regardless of which transition you fly, a procedure turn is required.

Some pilots mistakenly use the 295 radial from Mustang Vortac to intercept the NDB course at Dicey Intersection. This is not allowed. The 316 radial at 9000 feet, is the only transition route allowed from FMG to the IAF. You could also mistake the transition route from Pyram Intersection as a NoPT route, but this route only takes you to the NDB and you must remain at 10,500 feet until passing the NDB.

Let's assume we're at Nicer Intersection and cleared for the ap-

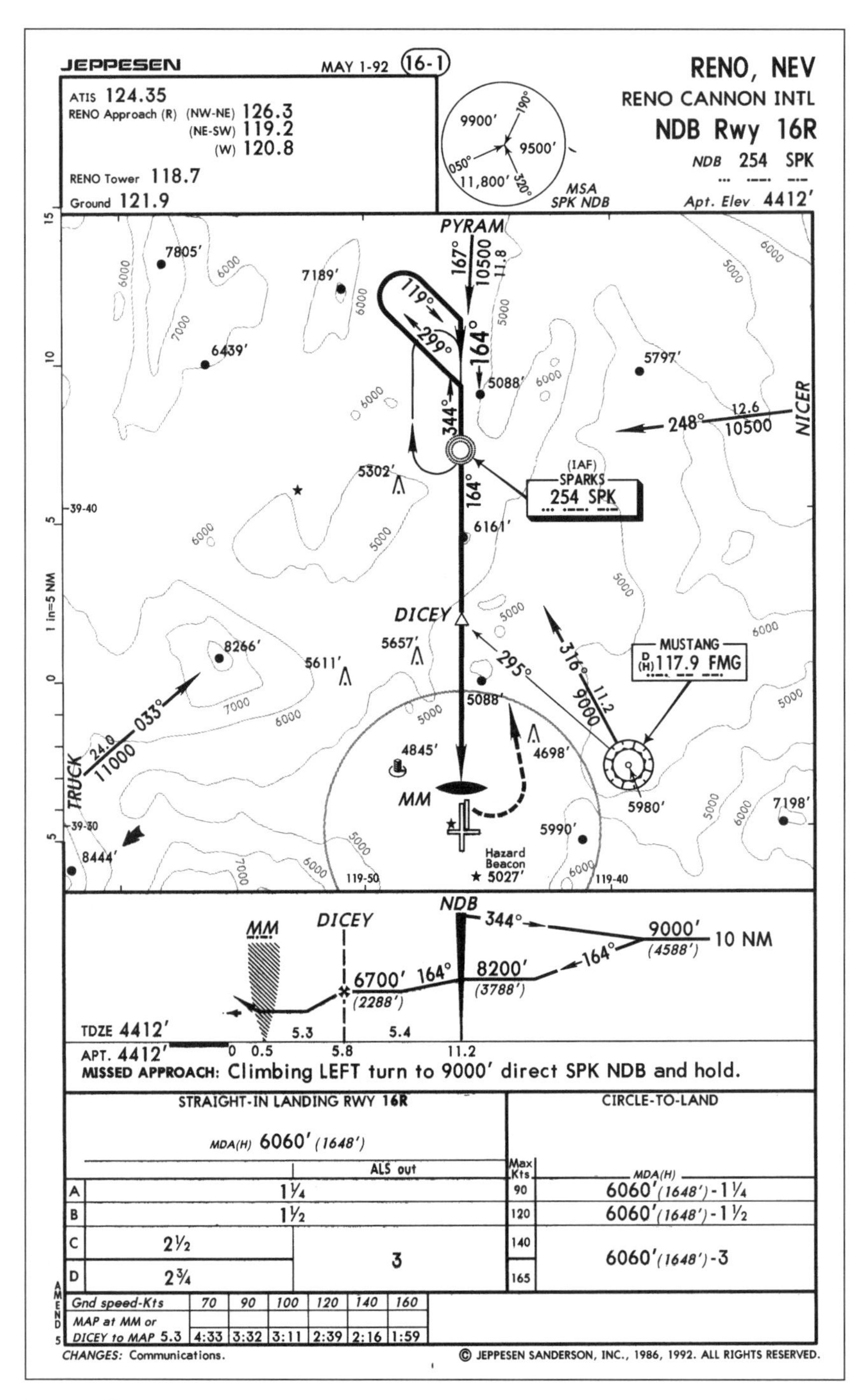
JEPPESEN
MAY 1-92 16-1
RENO, NEV
RENO CANNON INTL
NDB Rwy 16R
NDB 254 SPK
Apt. Elev 4412'
ATIS 124.35
RENO Approach (R) (NW-NE) 126.3
(NE-SW) 119.2
(W) 120.8
RENO Tower 118.7
Ground 121.9
9900'
9500'
11,800'
190°
050°
320°
MSA
SPK NDB
PYRAM
167°
10500
11.8
119°
299°
164°
344°
(IAF)
SPARKS
254 SPK
NICER
248°
12.6
10500
DICEY
MUSTANG
117.9 FMG
316°
11.2
9000
295°
TRUCK
033°
24.0
11000
MM
Hazard
Beacon
5027'
7805'
7189'
6439'
5088'
5797'
5302'
6161'
8266'
5611'
5657'
4845'
4698'
5980'
5990'
7198'
8444'
39-40
39-30
119-50
119-40
1 in=5 NM
NDB
344°
9000'
(4588')
10 NM
164°
8200'
(3788')
6700'
(2288')
TDZE 4412'
APT. 4412'
0 0.5 5.8 11.2
5.3 5.4
MISSED APPROACH: Climbing LEFT turn to 9000' direct SPK NDB and hold.
STRAIGHT-IN LANDING RWY 16R
CIRCLE-TO-LAND
MDA(H) 6060' (1648')
ALS out
Max Kts
A 1¼ 90 6060'(1648')-1¼
B 1½ 120 6060'(1648')-1½
C 2½ 3 140 6060'(1648')-3
D 2¾ 165
Gnd speed-Kts 70 90 100 120 140 160
MAP at MM or DICEY to MAP 5.3 4:33 3:32 3:11 2:39 2:16 1:59
AMEND 5
CHANGES: Communications.
© JEPPESEN SANDERSON, INC., 1986, 1992. ALL RIGHTS RESERVED.

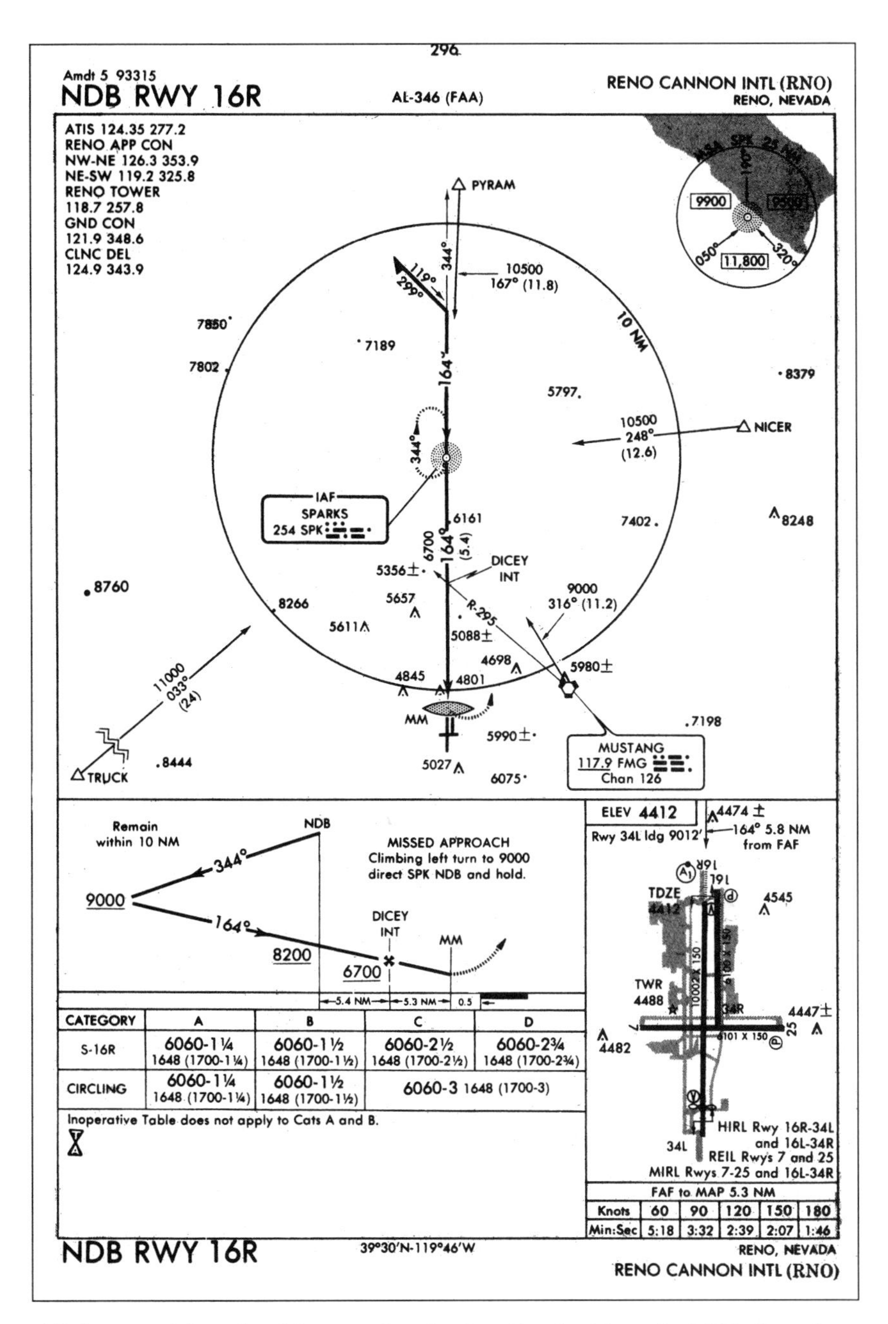

All the transitions for this procedure lead to Sparks (the only IAF). So unless you're radar vectored, you must always fly to Sparks first, then fly outbound and complete the procedure turn.

proach. For minimum effort we should:

• Track inbound to Sparks NDB on 248° at 10,500 feet. Turn right at Sparks to 30° (a suggested intercept heading) to intercept the outbound course of 344°. Note the time.

• Hold a heading of 30° until the head of the needle is 46 degrees off the tail. This is a relative bearing of 134.

• Turn left to 344° and maintain track and descend to 9000 feet. Set FMG VOR to the 295 radial for Dicey Intersection.

• After two or three minutes turn left to 299° and hold this heading until the head of the needle is 30 degrees off the tail. Then begin a standard rate turn to the right rolling out on 164° and you'll be on the inbound course regardless of the wind. Timing of this leg isn't necessary nor would it help. It's important that you be on track when you begin the procedure turn.

• Descend to 8200 feet and maintain a 164-degree track to Sparks. Lower the gear and flaps at Sparks, note time and descend to cross Dicey at 6700 feet. After crossing Dicey, descend to 6060 feet (the MDA).

• If a missed approach is necessary, start a climbing left turn to 9000 feet direct to the Sparks NDB. The magnetic track to Sparks would be whatever heading centered the needle after the missed. A teardrop holding entry would probably be necessary since 314° would be the closest outbound heading to your track to Sparks.

Now refer to the NDB-B chart to Lompoc, CA at right. In analyzing our options, there are two transition routes and two IAFs for this procedure. Note the profile view shows three step-down fixes from the Guadalupe VOR. This will add to the workload and will require strict attention to both altitude and drift corrections on final. In this situation, cross-check discipline will be important for a successful approach.

Assume we're cleared from the Gaviota Vortac transition to Perts. At first you might think this could be a NoPT procedure, but alas, it isn't.

• Fly the Gaviota 307 radial to intercept the 248 magnetic bearing to the Lompoc NDB. When the head of the needle is deflected 59 degrees to the left of the nose (307 - 248 = 59), we've intercepted the inbound course at Perts.

• Crossing Perts, turn left to 68°, the quickest way to enter the approach holding pattern and remain on the holding side. Descend to 3300 feet in the hold.

• Track 248° inbound while descending in accordance with the depicted step-down fixes. The gear and flaps should be extended not

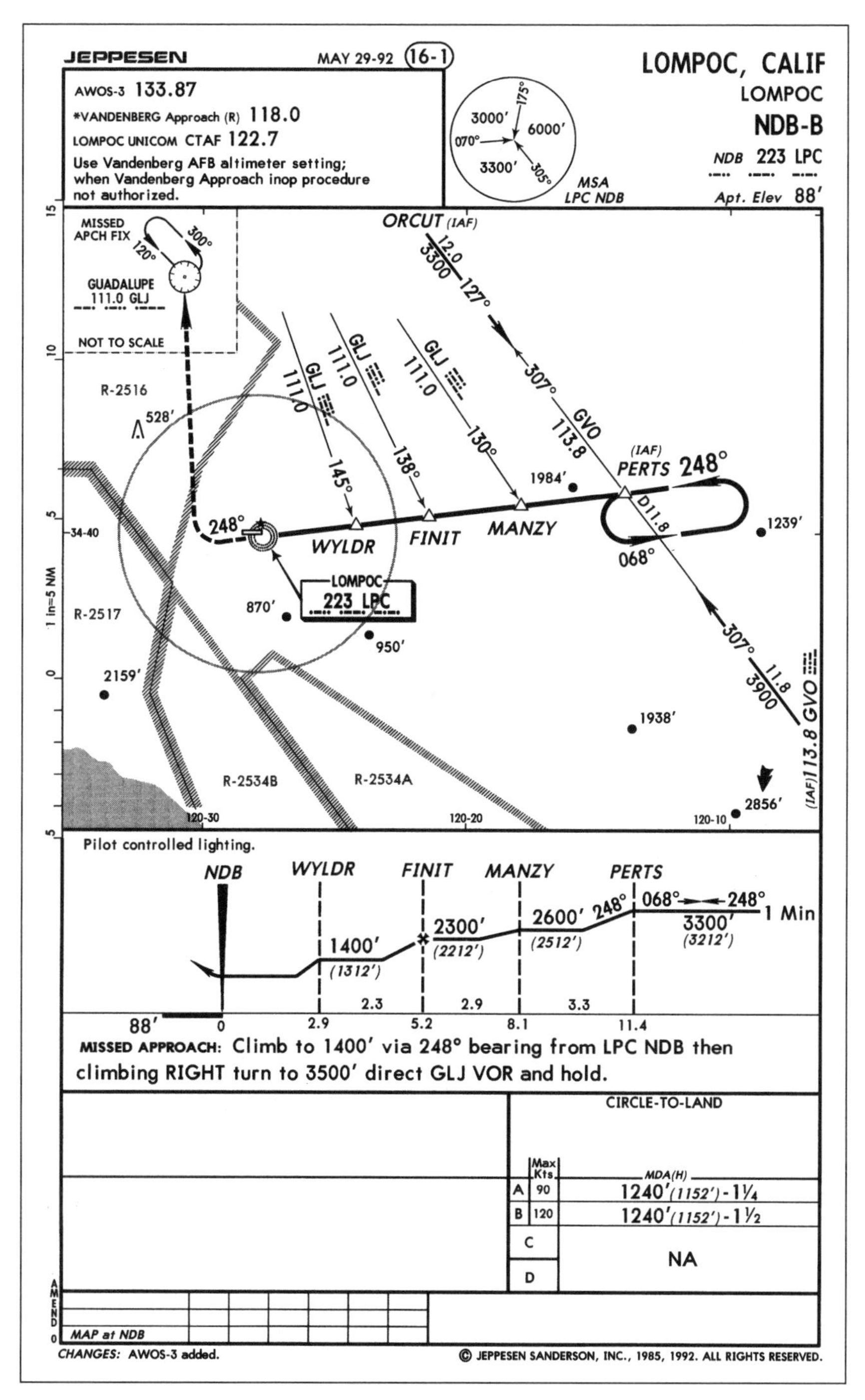
JEPPESEN
MAY 29-92 (16-1)
LOMPOC, CALIF
LOMPOC
NDB-B
NDB 223 LPC
Apt. Elev 88'
AWOS-3 133.87
*VANDENBERG Approach (R) 118.0
LOMPOC UNICOM CTAF 122.7
Use Vandenberg AFB altimeter setting; when Vandenberg Approach inop procedure not authorized.
3000'
6000'
3300'
175°
070°
305°
MSA
LPC NDB
MISSED APCH FIX
300°
120°
GUADALUPE
111.0 GLJ
NOT TO SCALE
ORCUT (IAF)
12.0
3300
127°
307°
GVO
113.8
GLJ
111.0
145°
138°
130°
R-2516
528'
1984'
(IAF)
PERTS 248°
D11.8
068°
1239'
248°
WYLDR
FINIT
MANZY
LOMPOC
223 LPC
870'
950'
R-2517
2159'
1938'
11.8
3900
(IAF) 113.8 GVO
R-2534B
R-2534A
2856'
34-40
120-30
120-20
120-10
1 in=5 NM
Pilot controlled lighting.
NDB
WYLDR
FINIT
MANZY
PERTS
068°
248°
1 Min
3300'
(3212')
2600'
(2512')
2300'
(2212')
1400'
(1312')
2.3
2.9
3.3
88'
0
2.9
5.2
8.1
11.4
MISSED APPROACH: Climb to 1400' via 248° bearing from LPC NDB then climbing RIGHT turn to 3500' direct GLJ VOR and hold.
CIRCLE-TO-LAND
Max Kts
MDA(H)
A 90 1240'(1152')-1¼
B 120 1240'(1152')-1½
C
D
NA
MAP at NDB
CHANGES: AWOS-3 added.
© JEPPESEN SANDERSON, INC., 1985, 1992. ALL RIGHTS RESERVED.

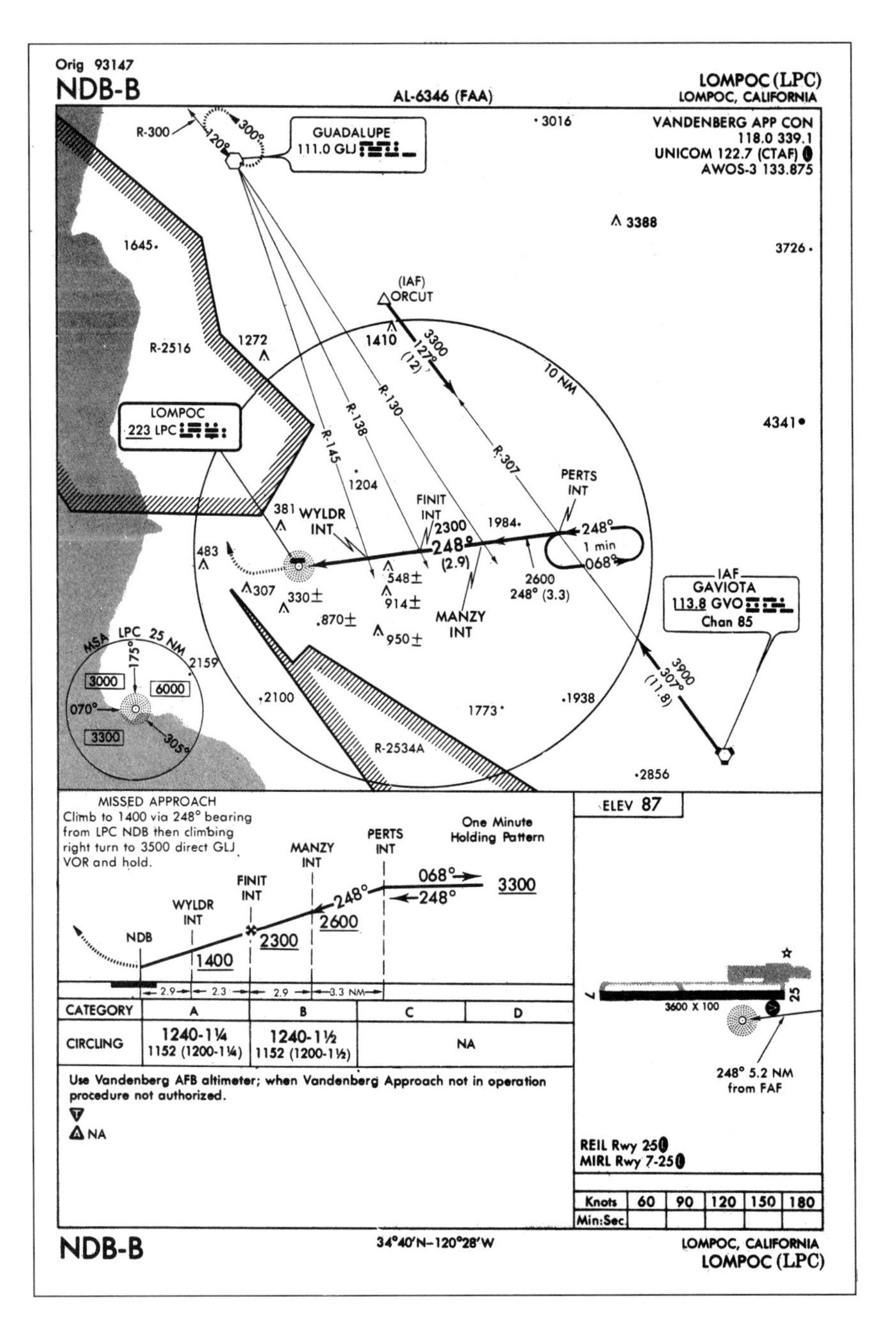

When proceeding to Perts from either the Orcut or Gaviota transitions, you must figure the relative bearing in advance so you can positively identify Perts intersection.

later than Wylder Intersection. Passing Wylder, descend to the MDA of 1240 feet. (If you flew the Orcut transition, you would execute a teardrop entry of 98° at Perts Intersection since that is the shortest way outbound on the holding side.)

The missed approach requires climbing to 1400 feet and tracking on the 248-degree bearing, then a climbing right turn to 3500 feet direct to the GLJ Vortac for holding. A teardrop entry appears to be the quickest entry at that location.

Many small airports will continue to have the NDB as the only instrument approach available. Bring back the old NDB approach from the back burner and sharpen those skills. You'll be glad you did.

The RNAV Approach

The RNAV approach is a rare beast, but it pays to know how it works. The reason for this is that In the Future When We All Have GPS (not really likely, but many more of us will have it than do now) a lot more approaches will be set up like this. We'll cover actual GPS overlay approaches in the next chapter.

Area Nav Approaches

RNAV approaches are some of the least commonly flown under IFR. The reason is due to a number of limiting factors. Only 15 percent of general aviation aircraft are equipped with RNAV compared to 60 percent which are ILS and VOR equipped. Based on equipment alone, only one out of four instrument pilots can fly an RNAV approach.

Not all RNAV computers are IFR certified and can legally be used for an approach. Certification may be for IFR en route or for IFR approaches, which requires a flight test of the aircraft in which the RNAV has been installed. For approaches, accuracy must be demonstrated within 0.4 nm over a surveyed test course. Some RNAV units cannot meet such requirements. Once certified, RNAVs never need to be recertified or checked for accuracy.

There are approximately 6000 published instrument approaches in the United States, of which only a few hundred are RNAV approaches. A scant handful (less than five) have an RNAV approach as the only instrument procedure.

According to Jeppesen, only two percent of its subscribers receive RNAV approach charts. Only a full U.S. RNAV terminal option is sold, which they encourage subscribers to keep under a separate tab. This decreases the likelihood that a pilot will realize that a field has an RNAV approach, even if he or she has the equipment needed to shoot it.

On the other hand, NOS includes RNAV approaches in each volume, printed in sequence with others to a particular field. They are also listed in the front of each volume by airport. However, NOS RNAV charts have some disadvantages which will be discussed shortly.

We have never been offered an RNAV approach by a controller even though we file with an RNAV suffix (/R). When we request an RNAV approach, the controller is often uncomfortable with the procedure.

High Workload

RNAV approaches increase pilot workload compared to a VOR or ILS approach. In addition to tuning the frequency, identifying a station and setting the OBS, the RNAV pilot must set the addresses of two or more waypoints. This requires the input of up to a seven digit number for each waypoint. Both degrees azimuth and distances are set to one decimal place accuracy. The more pilot input, the more chance for error.

During dual pilot operations, or if there is a helpful friend in the right seat, entries should be checked by both persons. All waypoints should be entered well ahead of the approach. For a typical approach, the minimum number of waypoint memories should be three. We prefer at least four so that the VOR itself can be designated as a waypoint to assist in orientation, in addition to the three waypoints that are part of the approach.

The original RNAV, called a course line computer (CLC), permits the input of a single waypoint at a time. This makes an instrument approach a feat of airmanship to be avoided. Similar to flying an intersection hold with only one VOR, while possible to do, it is not recommended as a safe practice. Changing RNAV addresses on final approach to an airport is an accident looking for a location.

Too Many Waypoints

FAA Advisory Circular 91-45 suggests that RNAV approaches to large airports might use six to ten waypoints! More rational cartographers typically avoid such mammoth procedures.

Due to the complexity of setting up an RNAV approach, a pilot should check for consistency among waypoints. Most approaches are flown in a straight line. Early in the approach, when aligned with the final approach course, the pilot should switch back and forth between the IAF and MAP waypoints to assure that there is no significant change in CDI needle indication and that the calculated distances between these waypoints match those indicated on the approach chart.

For example, while between the IAF and the MAP, the sum of the distances to these two points should match the distance indicated on the plate. If these distances do not match, *do not* continue the approach. The safest action may be to request an immediate turn toward a VOR for a hold at safe altitude while determining the error.

It may be unsafe to fly a missed approach to an RNAV defined fix. The address of this fix may also be in error and the point where the missed approach originates (the MAP) may not be correctly defined. A common error is to properly set the RNAV waypoint addresses, but base the approach on the wrong VOR/DME.

For these reasons, we find the NOS RNAV charts lacking. They often delete charting the VOR defining the procedure. In other cases, when the location of the VOR is indicated on the chart, its identifier and frequency are not! Jeppesen, on the other hand, goes out of its way to indicate the location and information regarding the controlling VOR, even if it is off the chart.

CDI Sensitivity

Most RNAV computers have an Approach Mode. This typically increases the CDI (or HSI) sensitivity to 1.25 nm full scale deflection (0.25 nm per dot). Using the approach mode does not change accuracy unless the RNAV has altitude compensation. Then the subtle difference between modes is that slant range correction is disabled when the approach mode is selected.

All RNAV approach chart DME distances are slant range and are not actual distances. Therefore, if you have one of the fancier lorans with altitude correction, there is a good reason to switch to the approach mode when flying an RNAV approach procedure in IMC. As the CDI sensitivity is increased by four, it is unwise to switch to the approach mode until the needle is well centered (one dot or less). Otherwise, the CDI will peg off scale.

When a procedure turn is flown, delay switching to the approach mode until inbound on the final approach course. It is easier to fly a procedure turn or holding pattern without the needle pegged when flying outbound. Once on final approach with the approach mode selected, course needle sensitivity requires small corrections similar to flying a localizer. Unlike a localizer, needle sensitivity does not change with proximity to the runway.

Lower Minimums, But....

Why then should you fly an RNAV approach, except to the few airports where you do not have a choice? At the other airports, an RNAV approach will result in a straight-in landing with lower minimums. The preferred runway for another type of approach may require a circle-to-land. The lower minimums may be possible due to course alignment or DME step-down fixes that avoid obstacles controlling other approaches. The RNAV minimums never equal those for a full ILS.

Some RNAV approaches are so complicated we would not choose to fly them to minimums. Refer to the accompanying chart for Ukiah, California, which is one of the more unusual approaches. This procedure requires a 60 degree turn to the left after reaching the MAP in order to reach the runway and then a second right turn of 70 degrees is required to align the aircraft with runway 33. You cannot expect to break out at minimums and accomplish these two turns and a descent within 0.9 nm of the runway.

This approach requires that you spot the runway at two statute miles (the visibility minimum), more reasonably three to four miles out to safely accomplish the side-step necessary for safe runway alignment, and descend 1826 feet from the MDA to the runway. The airport will be visible only through the right window at minimums!

Since both Jeppesen and NOS list waypoint addresses in latitude and longitude, it is tempting to use loran to fly the approach. This is strictly illegal, even if the loran is IFR certified.

The minimum requirements to fly an RNAV approach beyond that required for instrument flight are:

- RNAV approach charts
- an RNAV approved for IFR flight in your aircraft
- at least three programmed waypoint capability
- a VNAV computer if the glideslope will be flown

RNAV approaches have the following characteristics:

- They are usually aligned with the runway for a straight-in landing without turns.
- All the waypoints for a specific approach are usually based on the same VOR/DME. Jeppesen emphasizes this VOR/DME with a shadow box.
- The MAP is defined as an RNAV waypoint and the pilot must count down to this point.
- RNAV procedures are nonprecision, having no glideslope. However, a final approach angle (NOS) or Glide Slope Setting (Jeppesen) is published which allows VNAV to indicate a glideslope. This descent path is advisory and need not be flown. Unfortunately, its name suggests a legitimate ILS. Angles are typically 3.0 degrees, but may vary

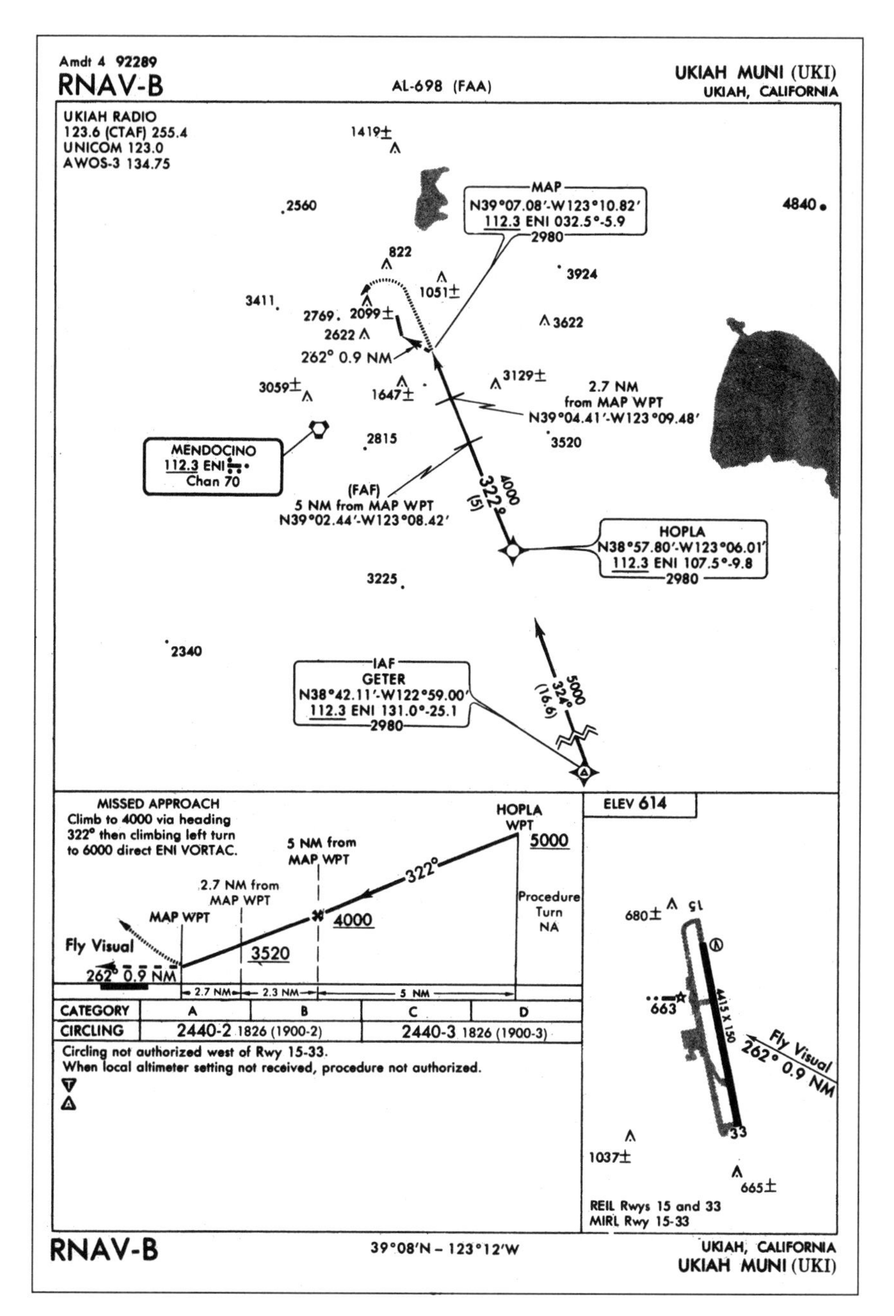

CATEGORY	A	B	C	D
CIRCLING	2440-2 1826 (1900-2)		2440-3 1826 (1900-3)	

The Ukiah, California RNAV-B approach is one of the hairiest you'll find. The fly-visual segment at the end is almost unreasonably demanding, requiring sharp turns in the last 0.9 mile.

from 2.5 to 3.5 degrees.

• A minimum of two, but more often three, waypoints define each approach; the initial approach fix (IAF), missed approach point (MAP) and missed approach holding fix. The IAF may double as the missed approach holding fix, in which case, the approach requires only two waypoints.

• The final approach fix (FAF) is not a defined waypoint, but is indicated as a distance from the MAP. Once at the IAF, a pilot should switch to the MAP waypoint and then not need to switch waypoints again unless a missed approach is necessary. Upon reaching the FAF, descent begins without any navigation switching.

• The VNAV glideslope may not be flown lower than the MDA, unless the field is in sight. Otherwise, a missed approach is likely. The closer the airplane is to the MAP while at MDA, the less likely the airplane can descend in time for a safe landing.

• A visual descent point (VDP), the point at the MDA in which a normal approach to landing can be accomplished, is implied where the VNAV glideslope crosses the MDA. The distance of the VDP from the MAP will be indicated on the profile view.

• Since RNAV procedures are not centered about a navaid, minimum safe altitudes (MSAs) are not indicated. It is worthwhile to review MSA information for other approaches to the same airport to assess surrounding terrain. RNAV approaches can be fun to fly and are among the most precise of nonprecision approaches. If properly equipped, try some practice approaches, so when necessary, they are in your bag of tricks when considering the safest approach to an airport. If you are not familiar with RNAV approaches, it is not a safe choice when operating in IMC.

GPS Overlay Approaches

In a strikingly uncharacteristic move, FAA threw its support behind new and promising technology a couple of years ago and endorsed the idea of using GPS for IFR operations, right up to and including actual approaches.

Well, the approaches have arrived, even if the receivers haven't. Though there are only two "real" GPS-only approaches at present (both special cases in Colorado for use only by one specific airline), there are actually a very large number of approaches that you could fly today, if you had an approach-approved GPS receiver.

These approaches are part of the GPS Overlay program instituted by FAA as a fast-track method to get GPS working in the real IFR world. The idea is simplicity itself: Just encode a few thousand existing non-precision approaches and put them into the databases of the new GPS receivers. Bingo—an instant GPS "infrastructure."

The execution, of course, is a bit more complicated than that. This chapter describes how it works.

The Next Generation Approach

Beginning with revisions sent out in early 1994, Jeppesen began to ship the first plates for GPS overlay approaches. Of course, until the equipment necessary to fly these approaches is available, the new plates are a mere curiosity; receivers certified to TSO C-129 aren't shipping as this book goes to press, but should be some time in the early summer of 1994.

So why are the plates being distributed early? Partly to get the jump on a logistical monster. There will be some 4,600 overlay approaches.

If they all got sent out at once, you'd be seeing the Mother of All Jepp Revisions. Unlike RNAV approach plates, all Jepp subscribers will be getting GPS overlay approach plates, whether they use GPS or not.

What about NOS? As this is written, no determination has been made as to how they'll deal with publishing the overlay approaches. According to FAA, there's no requirement to chart the approaches, but we think it highly unlikely that NOS will fail to do so.

What's an Overlay?

Overlay approaches are a means for FAA to take advantage of GPS technology without having to design new approaches specifically for it. Essentially, an overlay approach is simply an existing non-precision approach with specific pre-defined waypoints added to it. As we noted in the last chapter, leaving the pilot to program waypoints into a nav receiver opens the way for error to creep in. GPS approaches won't be prone to the pilot screwing up when entering waypoint data: It'll all be preprogrammed, so all the pilot has to do is call up the appropriate approach.

Experiments with GPS precision approaches notwithstanding, for the time being GPS will be usable only for non-precision approaches. The overlay program allows a pilot using the appropriate equipment to fly any variety of non-precision approach except LDA, SDF and localizer.

The GPS overlay program is being implemented in three phases:

• **Phase I.** This phase began before Initial Operational Capability (IOC) of the GPS satellite system was declared. During Phase I, GPS equipment could be used as the primary IFR flight guidance to fly non-precision approaches. The applicable non-precision approach navaid(s) required by the published procedure had to be active and monitored during the approach. IOC means there is a full constellation of 24 satellites, which occurred in December, 1993.

• **Phase II.** This phase begins after IOC is declared. GPS can be used as the primary IFR flight guidance during a non-precision approach without actively monitoring the applicable navaids defining the approach. However, the traditional ground-based navaid(s) required for the published approach must be operational and the associated avionics must be installed and operational, but need not be operating during the approach.

• **Phase III.** This phase begins after IOC and when the instrument approach has been modified to include GPS in the title of the published procedure. Neither the traditional aircraft avionics nor the ground station navaids need be installed, operational or monitored to fly the approach at the destination. However, at the alternate airport, the traditional ground-based and airborne navigational equipment defining the instrument approach procedure and route to the alternate must be installed and operational.

As this is written in spring, 1994, the program is transitioning from Stage II to Stage III. It should be a while before Phase III is fully up and running, but that's really an academic point: C-129-approved GPS receivers are going to be relatively rare for a while, FAA isn't about to go around shutting off NDBs and VORs, and nobody in his right mind would fly an IFR airplane without the avionics necessary to fly a traditional approach on board in the first place. So the special abilities Phase III offers won't do the average pilot much good for the immediate future, anyway.

Waypoint Database

Unlike existing avionics, which rely on the pilot to dial in a frequency and OBS setting, then follow along on a paper chart, or manually program waypoints as is the case with RNAV, approach-approved GPS receivers have entire approaches stored within them. It's this waypoint database that makes the whole idea of GPS approaches practical.

As a result, there will be a significant number of new waypoints inserted in these databases.

For the most part, the new waypoints are nothing more than the positions of existing fixes, which allows a GPS receiver to follow along as the approach proceeds. The actual routes flown are the same as on the existing, underlying approach.

Some of the waypoints, however, correspond to reference points on the approach that weren't rigidly defined before. For example, a GPS overlay approach will have not only the IAF and FAF in the database, but the MAP as well.

In addition to these new waypoints and "canned" approaches, the databases will have the usual navaids and intersections already found in database GPS and loran receivers, plus SIDs and STARs. Naturally, they must be updated periodically and must maintain a high degree of integrity.

All overlay approaches have (as a minimum) waypoints for the initial approach fix (IAF), final approach fix (FAF), missed approach point (MAP) and the missed approach holding point (MAHP). Intermediate fixes and named step-down fixes may also be included.

Waypoints at the MAP and MAHP are treated as fly-over versus fly-by fixes, meaning that the pilot must actually cross directly over the waypoint as opposed to passing by it. By contrast, an IAF can be a fly-by fix: The controller can vector you so that you don't have to cross it, but that can't be done with the MAP, for obvious reasons.

Wherever possible, waypoints will use the same name as in the existing non-precision approach. If the fix in the existing procedure isn't named, a descriptive naming convention will be used, e.g., RW35 for the threshold of Runway 35. There is a five-character limitation, so some waypoint names may be a little cryptic. For example, the 255-radial/7-DME arc IAF for the Yuma VOR 17 (see chart on pp103) will be named D225G. As noted above, in some instances waypoints will be added that don't exist on a current approach, such as an FAF on a no-FAF approach.

The visual descent point is another fix on some current approaches that won't be included in an overlay approach. Instead of DME fixes, along track distances (ATD) will be used. On the Yuma VOR procedure, for example, the 5-DME fix could be identified as 1.0 ATD to the RW17 waypoint (the missed approach point).

The Yuma approach also uses a final approach course fix (FACF) to identify the 7-DME fix. FACF waypoints are used to define intermediate fixes along the procedure ground track. On the Yuma approach, the CF17 waypoint defines the final approach path with a dogleg at the FAF (more on this later).

Although it isn't required, some approach charts have the GPS waypoints labeled on the chart. The charts might appear cluttered, but flying the approach without the waypoints labeled could be confusing. If your GPS receiver has a map display, orientation during the approach is easier.

Pilots will use a control display unit to select an approach. Depending on the unit, you'll select the desired approach from a list of available approaches at an airport. For approaches with multiple IAFs, you'll select the approach and then the desired IAF to arrange the correct sequence of waypoints. Automatic sequencing will be used between fly-by waypoints to help you lead turns and maintain centerline on the approach (this is another implication of a fly-over waypoint; by definition, if you fly over the waypoint, you'll go past the new course centerline).

Positional Awareness

Since you need an approved receiver to fly the approaches, and since the receiver has to have all the waypoints in its database, isn't the approach plate, well...redundant? Not exactly. For one thing, the over-

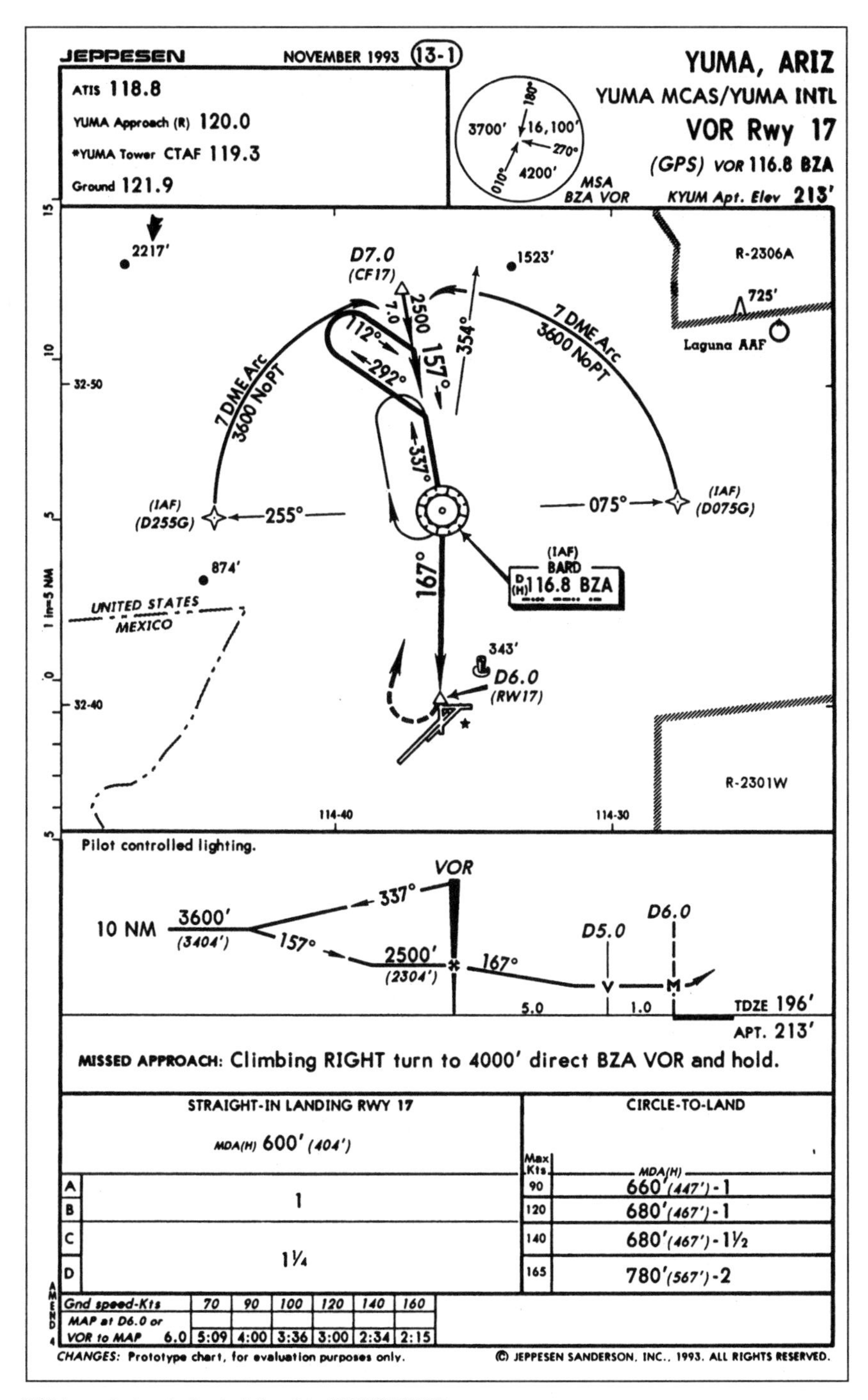

	STRAIGHT-IN LANDING RWY 17 MDA(H) 600' (404')	Max Kts	CIRCLE-TO-LAND MDA(H)
A	1	90	660'(447')-1
B	1	120	680'(467')-1
C	1¼	140	680'(467')-1½
D	1¼	165	780'(567')-2

Gnd speed-Kts	70	90	100	120	140	160
MAP at D6.0 or VOR to MAP 6.0	5:09	4:00	3:36	3:00	2:34	2:15

lay database includes horizontal fixes but no vertical information. So, as with a conventional approach, you're on your own to determine stepdown altitudes and descent to the MDA.

Then there's the matter of positional awareness. When you're letting down through thick gray clouds, you might want something a little more substantial than your imagination to help with situational awareness. Overall, the GPS overlays look like conventional approaches. But they do have some unfamiliar features that relate directly to the way GPS navigation works.

Because it's an earth-referenced, area navigation system, GPS works in the TO-TO mode, meaning that the receiver navigates towards a fix and not away from one, as with VOR. In the short term, this peculiarity will yield an explosion of new, named intersections. Let's look at a couple.

Many conventional approaches have transitions that begin at a VOR and proceed outbound (FROM-FROM) until intersecting an intermediate- or final-approach segment at an unnamed intersection. As noted above, this won't work with GPS. The box has to be navigating toward a fix that's stored in its database. One example of this is shown on the Yuma approach, as fix CF17.

"CF" means capture fix; it's a synthetic intersection placed there solely so the receiver will have a way to navigate TO a point in space from which it can proceed along the final approach course to the next fix. As the receiver cycles through the various approach fixes, the intersections will appear on the display exactly as they are depicted on the chart.

The DME arc depicted on the Yuma chart uses yet another intersection nomenclature. "D255G" means that the IAF intersection is on the 255-degree radial, at a DME distance of seven miles. How do we know it's seven miles? The "G" corresponds to DME distance: A is one mile, B is two, and so on. This is an ARINC standard—don't ask us why it's done this way. As we said, eventually the intersection will carry a five-letter name (which, for that matter, doesn't make any sense either...but it's easier to remember).

One of the technical challenges that GPS manufacturers have had to meet is to develop a means of adjusting CDI sensitivity. For terminal-area flight, the CDI needs to have 3-mile sensitivity, but on the approach, it has to automatically switch to approach mode and smoothly shift to 0.3-mile sensitivity. (Contrast all of this highly automated operation to the workings of an RNAV receiver as described in the last chapter.)

But how does the receiver know when to switch to the finer resolution? The logical solution would have been to pick some fixed point on the approach, such as the final approach fix. But as we noted above, quite a few non-precision approaches have no FAF, so, again, a synthetic intersection was devised to give the GPS receiver a reference point.

This synthetic fix is called a sensor FAF and an example of one is shown on the NDB 23 overlay approach for Sumter, South Carolina (page 106). In both the plan and profile views, the note (FF23) identifies the sensor FAF. Sumter's NDB is a type of approach known in the TERPs trade as an "on-airport, no FAF," meaning that the procedure has a navaid on the airport but does not have a conventional final-approach fix.

The sensor FAF is placed at a point four miles from the end of the runway. Approaches that have a real FAF won't need the sensor FAF (nor will one be depicted) since the CDI will automatically shift when crossing that fix.

Despite the fact that it's needed for technical reasons, we like the sensor FAF idea. NDB approaches that lack a final-approach fix give true meaning to the word "non-precision," especially when they're flown behind an ADF with all the selectivity of a Marconi spark-gap receiver.

Some non-FAF approaches have long inbound segments, and the sensor FAF provides a definite fix on the way to the airport. As GPS proves itself and pure GPS procedures are designed, sensor FAFs will probably become the equivalent of real FAFs in the TERPs world. That may yield lower minimums at some airports (for a full discussion of TERPs and approach design, see Volume 3 of the Instrument Pilot's Library, *Charts and Plates*).

Another useful addition to overlay approaches is the nautical-mile distance from a step-down or final-approach fix to a timed missed-approach point. Back when Captain Jepp invented instrument approaches, a stopwatch was the only way to determine when it was time to give it up, cob the throttle and head for another airport. With DME, loran and now GPS, timing finishes a weak fourth place as a means of finding the missed-approach point.

Flying an Approach

Lets review a typical implementation for a GPS overlay procedure at Yuma, AZ. This approach can be initiated from one of three IAF waypoints: Bard or two different DME arcs. After selecting the approach and the desired IAF, the waypoints are automatically arranged in the proper sequence to fly the procedure. Upon selecting the ap-

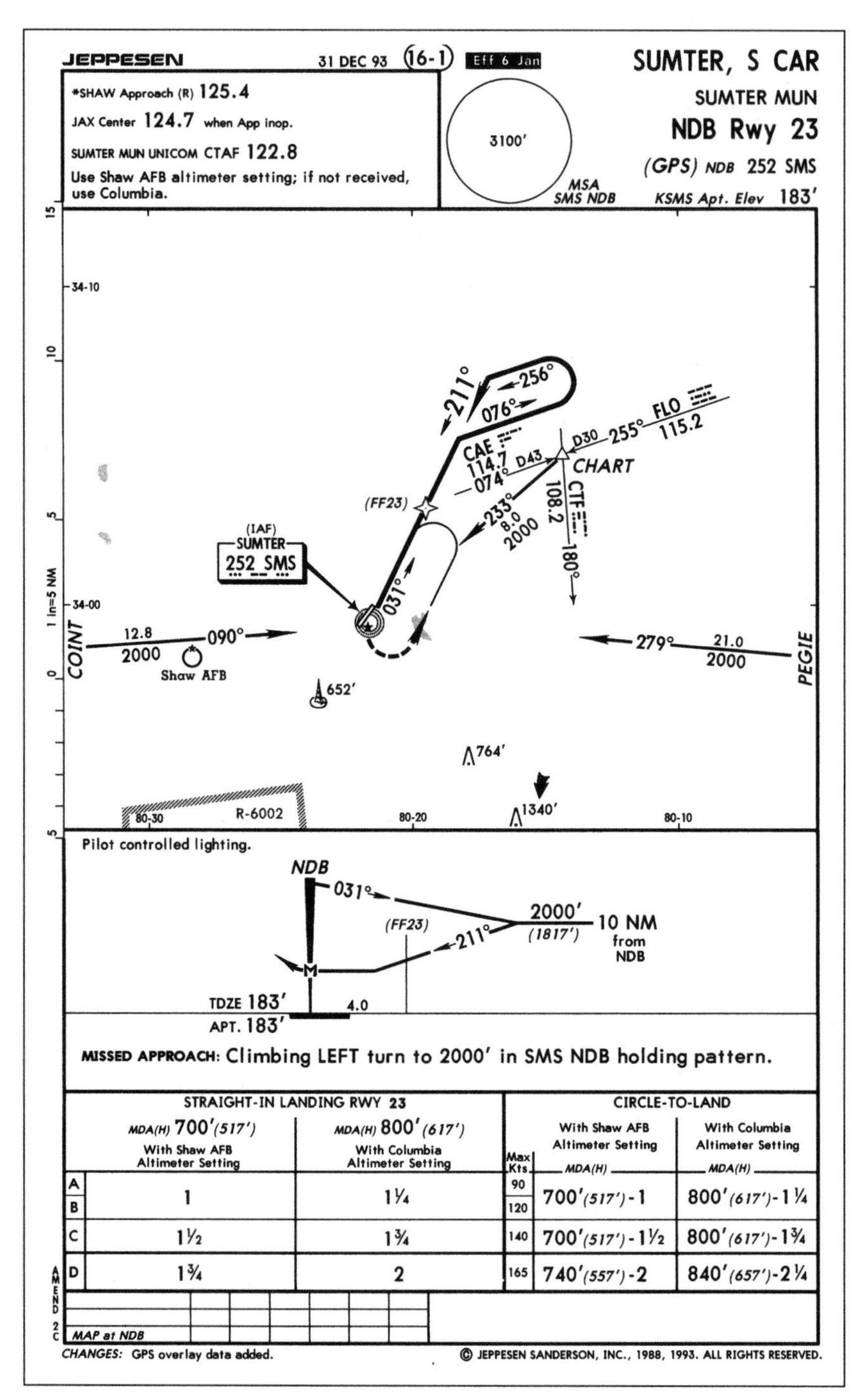
JEPPESEN
31 DEC 93
16-1
Eff 6 Jan
SUMTER, S CAR
SUMTER MUN
NDB Rwy 23
(GPS) NDB 252 SMS
KSMS Apt. Elev 183'
*SHAW Approach (R) 125.4
JAX Center 124.7 when App inop.
SUMTER MUN UNICOM CTAF 122.8
Use Shaw AFB altimeter setting; if not received, use Columbia.
3100'
MSA SMS NDB
34-10
34-00
256°
076°
211°
FLO 115.2
D30 255°
CAE 114.7
D43
074°
CHART
108.2 CTF
180°
(FF23)
233° 8.0 2000
(IAF) SUMTER 252 SMS
031°
COINT
12.8
2000
090°
Shaw AFB
279°
21.0
2000
PEGIE
652'
764'
1340'
R-6002
80-30
80-20
80-10
1 in=5 NM
Pilot controlled lighting.
NDB
031°
2000'
(1817')
10 NM from NDB
(FF23)
211°
M
TDZE 183'
4.0
APT. 183'
MISSED APPROACH: Climbing LEFT turn to 2000' in SMS NDB holding pattern.
STRAIGHT-IN LANDING RWY 23
MDA(H) 700'(517') With Shaw AFB Altimeter Setting
MDA(H) 800'(617') With Columbia Altimeter Setting
CIRCLE-TO-LAND
With Shaw AFB Altimeter Setting MDA(H)
With Columbia Altimeter Setting MDA(H)
Max Kts
A B 1 1¼ 90 120 700'(517')-1 800'(617')-1¼
C 1½ 1¾ 140 700'(517')-1½ 800'(617')-1¾
D 1¾ 2 165 740'(557')-2 840'(657')-2¼
AMEND 2C
MAP at NDB
CHANGES: GPS overlay data added.
© JEPPESEN SANDERSON, INC., 1988, 1993. ALL RIGHTS RESERVED.

proach, the GPS equipment provides a +/- 1.0 nm linear CDI scale during terminal navigation until 2 nm from the FAF.

Commencing the approach from Bard, the sequence is BZA (IAF), BZA (FAF), RW17 threshold (MAP) and BZA (MAHP). The Bard waypoint serves as the IAF, FAF and MAHP. After crossing Bard outbound, the GPS equipment switches to to/from navigation either manually or automatically, depending on the manufacturer design. The course reversal maneuver for the procedure turn is flown using to/from navigation and normal VOR procedures.

Automatic Sequencing

Once on the inbound course, either you or the equipment (depending on manufacturer design) switches to automatic sequencing and to/to navigation. An along track distance (ATD) is provided to the FAF. At two nautical miles to the FAF, the equipment automatically switches from a +/- 1.0 nm linear CDI scale to a +/- 0.3 nm CDI scale.

At the FAF, the equipment automatically sequences to the RW17 (MAP). When the distance is 1.0 ATD, you're at the visual descent point. It's important to remember on this approach that the distances are relative to the MAP, not the FAF.

The MAP is named RW17. At this waypoint, the equipment automatically switches to manual sequencing and you must intentionally initiate the missed approach function. Once activated, the equipment sequences to the MAHP and switches to to/from operation and provides positive course guidance to the MAHP and the holding function.

Arc Approach

Commencing the approach from the BZA 255-radial/7-mile arc IAF (D255G), the sequence of waypoints is D255G (IAF), BZA (to/from navigation for the arc), CF17 (final approach course fix to establish the final course to the FAF), BZA (FAF), RW17 (MAP) and BZA (MAHP). When selecting the approach, to/to navigation is provided to the IAF for the fix-to-fix. The equipment automatically sequences (depending on the design) at the IAF to the BZA waypoint and switches to to/from navigation to enable you to use normal procedures for flying the arc and determining the lead radial.

Depending on the design, the CF17 waypoint may be used to establish the 157-degree course to the FAF. This can be accomplished by momentarily sequencing to the CF17 waypoint and then immediately to the FAF using to/to navigation. Another alternative is to use to/from navigation and VOR procedures all the way to the FAF. At two nautical miles from the FAF, the equipment will automatically adjust the CDI scaling from linear +/- 1.0 nm to +/- 0.3 nm and the remainder of the approach and missed approach would remain unchanged.

Interim Capability

Overlay approaches are interim procedures, allowing an early capability for GPS-equipped aircraft to fly existing non-precision approaches. Since existing non-precision approaches are based on ground-based navaids, the Overlay procedures use to/to and to/from navigation guidance. Approaches designed specifically for GPS will use to/to navigation only and will take full advantage of the accuracy and flexibility of satellite navigation.

While on the surface the overlay approaches seem simple enough, we suspect that initially, they won't be quite as simple as the FAA has promised. We're sure lots of questions will arise once the first approach-based boxes hit the market.

Back Course Approaches

"Fly away from the needle...fly away from the needle, fly away from the needle...." This was our mantra as we flew our first back course during instrument training in the company Mooney. Though the airplane was well equipped, with a King RNAV, HSI, and so forth, half the goodies were usually broken. In this case, it was the RNAV, which had gone toes-up en route, leaving us with only the second navcom and no way to hook it into the HSI. There was the usual low cloud layer and fog over Nantucket, which is where we were headed. We broke out about 100 feet above minimums and could just make out the lights through the murk. It was our first and last real, live back course approach (we haven't needed one since), and in retrospect one of the most satisfying.

It's not often you'll be given a back course approach, which is a good thing since they can be devilishly confusing. We have the idea of flying towards the needle drilled into us from day one of our instrument training, and it feels distinctly odd to reverse that thinking. Still, they can be useful. Here's how they work.

The Eccentric Approach

We train and train and train pilots to avoid bad habits during instrument flight. One principle that we drill into their brains is to avoid reverse sensing on any needle...and then we teach back course approaches as the exception to that rule.

We once had a CFII candidate who was an excellent instrument pilot. His preparation was flawless. The day of his flight test, we rode with him to the airport where the test would take place. On the way in, we flew a practice back course approach. Imagine our surprise when he tried to fly it like a normal localizer. Perhaps it was the anxiety of the flight test which prompted him to do this. Fortunately, he flew the back course properly during the checkride.

Back Course Peculiarities

There are several anomalies to flying back course approaches, the first of which is that you must develop a mental set and must tell yourself, 'This is a back course approach and I will fly *reverse* sensing.' This is akin to a seaplane pilot operating an amphibious aircraft. When landing in water, the pilot must say, "This is a water landing, therefore, I will land with the wheels *up*," which is not normal when flying an airplane with wheels attached.

And so it is with the back course localizer; not only must we tell ourselves that the CDI won't behave normally, but it will also be more sensitive than the front course localizer. Oh yes, there's one other item; a back course marker (when used) will illuminate a different marker beacon light. Do you remember which one? It's the white light and the Morse code is unusual (two dots, a pause and two dots). Finally, there's the problem of false glideslope indications if the front course is a full ILS (the glideslope signal can be picked up on the back course, but the indications it gives are *not* valid!).

You'd think that there would be many more of these approaches, since there are nearly a thousand full or partial ILS facilities in the U.S. Every front course localizer has a back course, so that would provide an approach facility to either end of the runway.

However, the FAA has replaced many of the old tube-type localizer transmitters with solid state transmitters (and every new transmitter installed today is solid state), with a result that not every localizer has a back course of sufficient signal strength to establish an approach procedure. We now have much more reliable front courses, but the back courses aren't always available.

Greater Sensitivity

A back course approach is a non-precision procedure with higher minima than a full ILS, but it can get you down to a respectable altitude due to accurate course guidance. The CDI will be more sensitive than when flying the front course due to the fact that the localizer transmitter is located at the back course end of the runway. In some instances, the transmitter may be displaced as much as 1,000 feet from the approach end of the runway. As a result, at any given point during a back course approach, you are always closer to the localizer transmitter than when on the front course.

The front course localizer is normally 700 feet wide at the runway threshold. The back course localizer may be only 400 feet wide at the threshold and if the transmitter is close to the threshold, the back course may have a width of zero at the threshold! Your CDI is four times as sensitive when flying a normal ILS, so imagine how sensitive it is in this situation.

Which Side of Centerline?

Reminding yourself that a back course requires flying away from the needle can be helpful, but the CDI can also assist you. In this situation, the needle isn't telling you where to go but where you are. For example, if the needle deflects to the right, you are right of centerline and should correct left to intercept.

If the aircraft you fly has a CDI with the blue and yellow bands on the bottom of the indicator, keep in mind that the needle will point to the colored sector of the localizer in which you are located. (On the back course, blue is the left side of the localizer and yellow is on the right.)

Two basic principles used when flying a front course also apply during back course approaches. These are the concept of course and reference heading. The course is the desired track to be followed along the ground. If there is a crosswind, the heading you fly will differ from the course as you crab in order to keep the needle centered. Thus, the course may be 270°, but a heading of 250° may be needed for tracking.

The Approach

Refer to the approach chart for the back course Runway 27L at Melbourne, Florida on the next page. If you flew the full approach without the aid of radar vectors, it's likely that you would fly to the Melbourne VOR, track outbound to Capen Intersection and fly the one minute holding pattern to reverse course.

Suppose you decide to fly the front course out from the VOR to Capen, a distance of 5.2 nm. The CDI will have proper sensing while tracking to Capen, but will have reverse sensing after turning inbound. This is where confusion can reign. As you reverse direction in the holding pattern, the needle will appear to indicate in reverse. Let's say there's a north wind and the CDI swings to the left as you turn inbound to a heading of 270°.

When flying a front course in this situation, the needle would be on your right. But you're on the back course now and the needle remains on the left. If you correct to the right to intercept, the CDI will approach the course from the left, the same as the airplane. If you drift off the

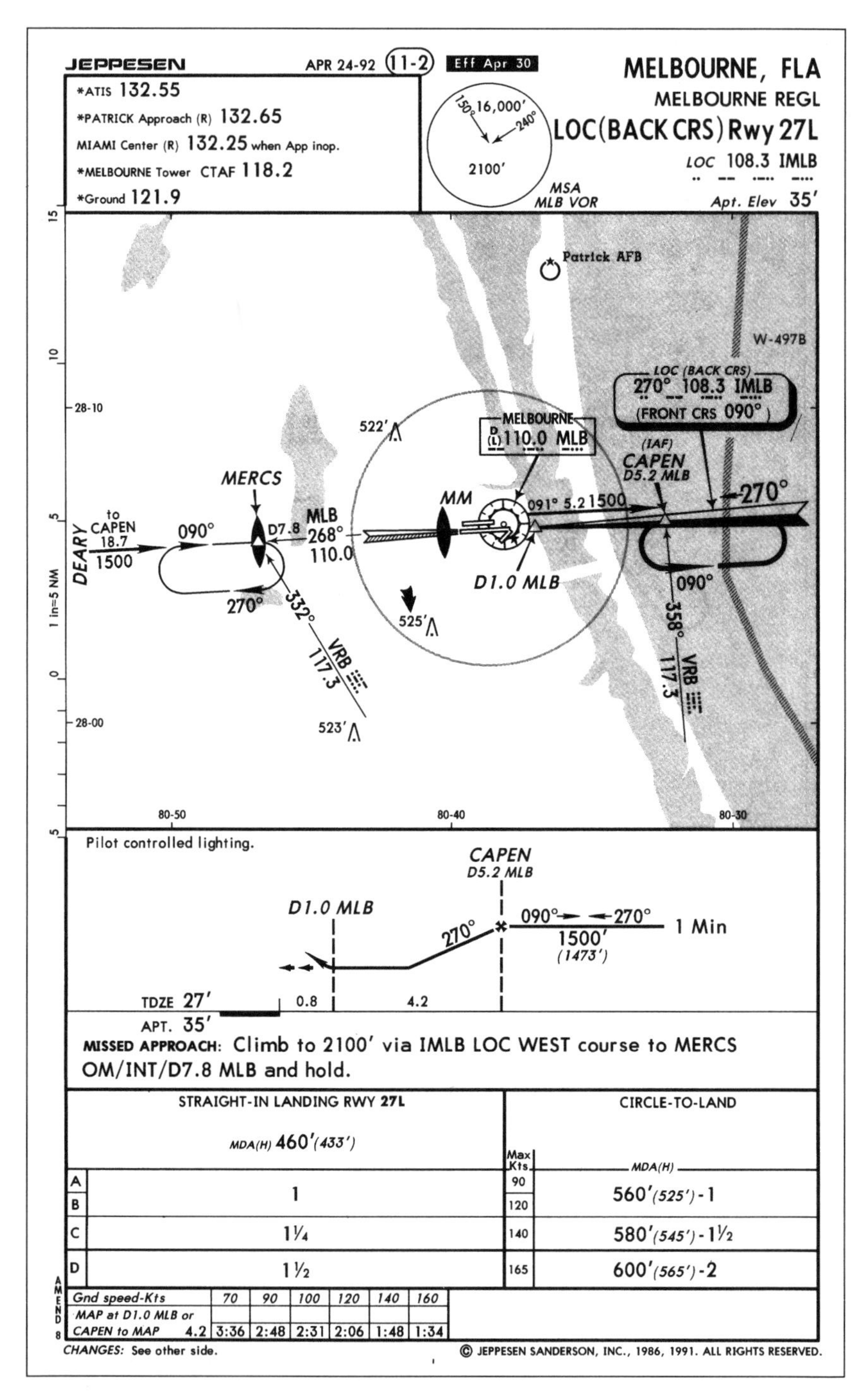

JEPPESEN
APR 24-92 (11-2) Eff Apr 30
MELBOURNE, FLA
MELBOURNE REGL
LOC(BACK CRS) Rwy 27L
LOC 108.3 IMLB
Apt. Elev 35'
*ATIS 132.55
*PATRICK Approach (R) 132.65
MIAMI Center (R) 132.25 when App inop.
*MELBOURNE Tower CTAF 118.2
*Ground 121.9
16,000'
2100'
MSA MLB VOR
Patrick AFB
W-497B
LOC (BACK CRS) 270° 108.3 IMLB (FRONT CRS 090°)
MELBOURNE 110.0 MLB
(IAF) CAPEN D5.2 MLB
091° 5.2 1500
270°
MERCS
MM
D7.8
MLB 268° 110.0
to CAPEN 18.7 1500
DEARY
090°
270°
332°
VRB 117.3
D1.0 MLB
090°
358°
522'
525'
523'
28-10
28-00
80-50
80-40
80-30
1 in=5 NM
Pilot controlled lighting.
CAPEN D5.2 MLB
D1.0 MLB
090° 270° 1 Min
1500' (1473')
TDZE 27'
APT. 35'
0.8
4.2
MISSED APPROACH: Climb to 2100' via IMLB LOC WEST course to MERCS OM/INT/D7.8 MLB and hold.
STRAIGHT-IN LANDING RWY 27L
MDA(H) 460'(433')
CIRCLE-TO-LAND
Max Kts
MDA(H)
A B 1 90 120 560'(525')-1
C 1¼ 140 580'(545')-1½
D 1½ 165 600'(565')-2
Gnd speed-Kts 70 90 100 120 140 160
MAP at D1.0 MLB or CAPEN to MAP 4.2 3:36 2:48 2:31 2:06 1:48 1:34
CHANGES: See other side.
© JEPPESEN SANDERSON, INC., 1986, 1991. ALL RIGHTS RESERVED.

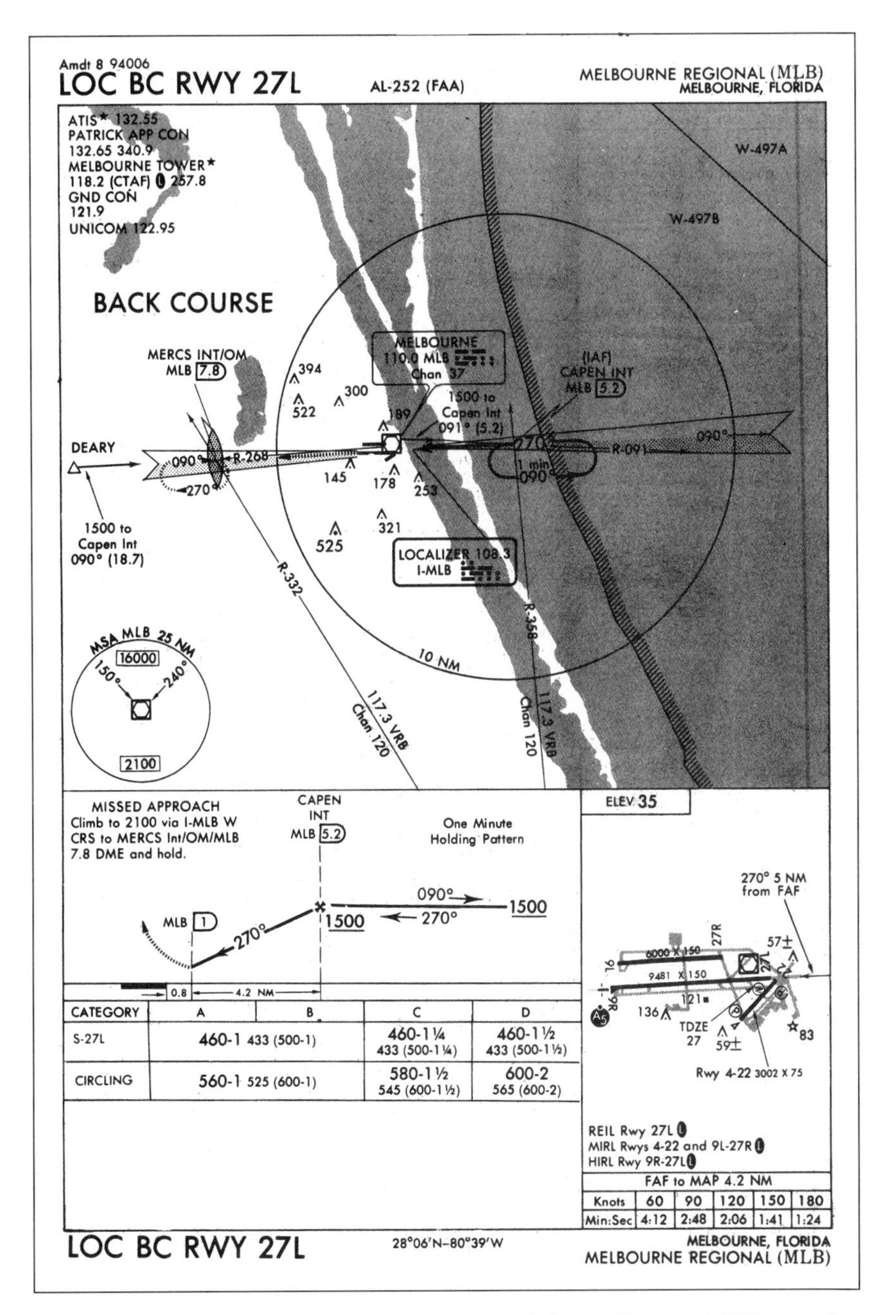

Note that Capen is defined by Vero Beach and the Melbourne VOR, not the localizer. To legally identify it you need to have the VOR tuned in, but in practical terms the localizer will serve. Just be careful of reverse sensing.

centerline, the needle will point in the direction the airplane is drifting. On the back course, the CDI does not point to the centerline as it does on the front course, but instead it points to the side of the centerline that the airplane is on.

Ignore all glideslope indications when flying a back course procedure, unless the procedure is outfitted with one, and these are few and far between. Many approach charts list the notation to "Disregard glide slope indications." Regardless of whether the warning is there, don't be attempted by what appears to be a usable signal. It's an invitation to disaster.

Back Course and More

Refer to the approach chart on the right for the back course procedure to Reno, Nevada. After reviewing the profile section, if the reverse sensing doesn't drive you crazy while flying this procedure, the series of DME stepdown fixes will. Notice that, after all that stepping down, the best you can do is a circling approach! It's due to obstacles in the final approach area.

The missed approach instructions require a climb to 10,000 feet on the north course localizer to the Sparks NDB for holding. You'll still have reverse sensing as you fly the localizer out.

If you execute the missed approach from a circling maneuver, the localizer must be intercepted to fly out to Sparks. Obstacle protection is very important in this case as you climb from circling minimums to 10,000 feet. Remember, the CDI will still point to the side of the localizer you're on, so make your turn back to the centerline.

To our eye, this approach is chock-full of places to make mistakes. There are six step-down fixes, and reverse sensing all the way...including the missed approach. If we had to fly this to minimums, we'd think about going elsewhere.

Helpful Devices

To avoid the reverse sensing game, you can fly an airplane with a horizontal situation indicator (HSI). The beauty of the HSI is that, if you set the OBS to the front course heading (164° for the Reno procedure), you will have proper CDI sensing.

Also, an autopilot with the reverse sensing feature can help, and one with an approach mode which will accommodate the greater sensitivity of the localizer is better yet.

Even without these devices, operations on the back course need not be considered the dark side of the force, if you keep your head set and remember what the CDI is telling you.

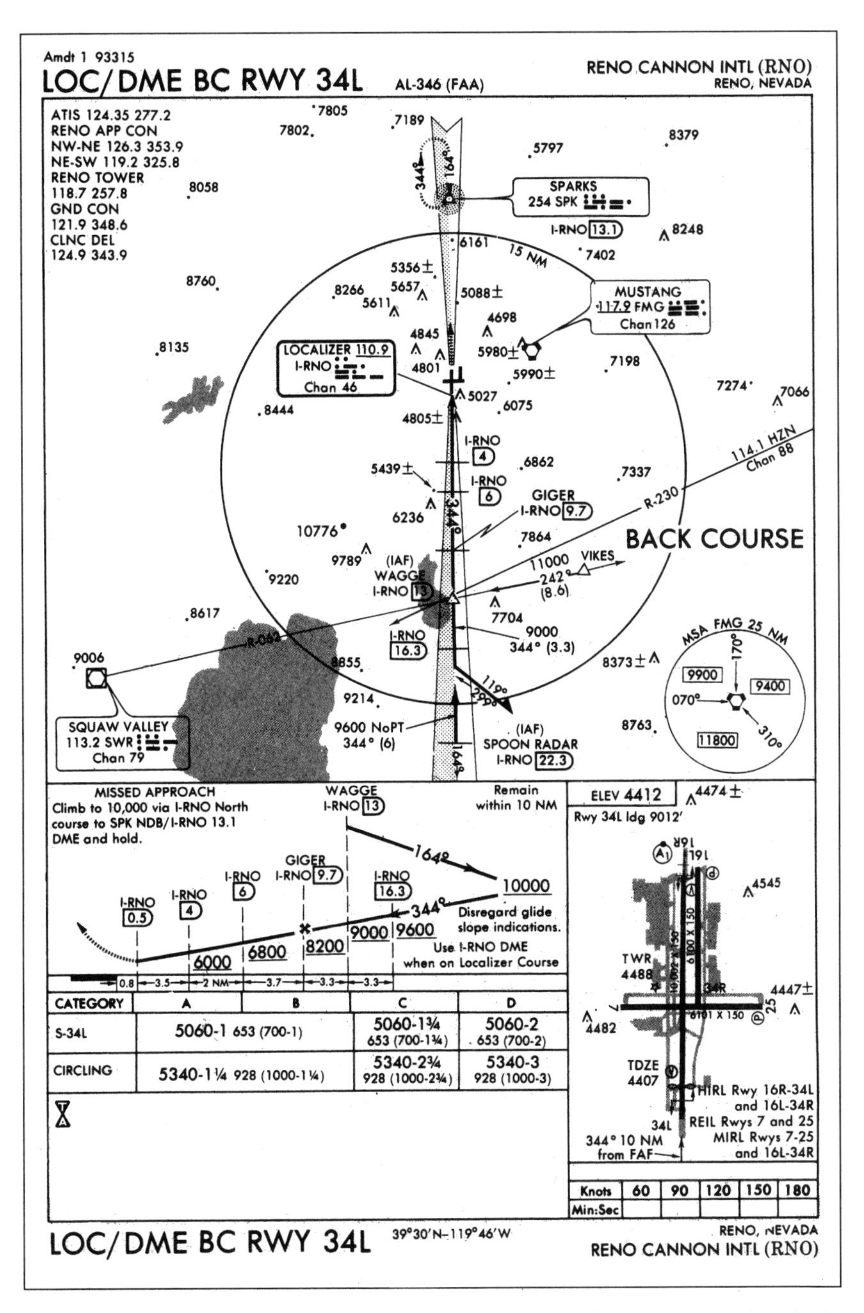

Not only must you deal with a needle that wants to go the wrong way, just look at all those step-down fixes (six, with the last only 1.8 miles from the MAP). That's a lot to keep track of on an approach.

Ground Controlled Approaches

So what do you do if you're up there in the soup and lose all of your electrics? If you're a wise pilot, you'll have a handheld radio (with fresh *batteries, folks) with which you can contact ATC and ask for a ground controlled approach. If you're a really wise pilot, you'll have an external antenna for said handheld installed so you can talk to someone a reasonable distance away. If you're an exceptionally wise pilot, you'll also have a portable GPS, which will, in an emergency, allow you to fly a for-real non-precision approach (but that's another story).*

The ground controlled approach is the only way of getting down that doesn't rely on on-board navigation equipment. It's rare that all your nav radios will be out, leaving your comm intact; that's why it's a good idea to carry a handheld. If you're going to lose equipment, it'll probably be the whole deal at once.

As an Air Force F-16 pilot, contributor J. Ross Russo is well qualified to discuss both the civilian version of the ground controlled approach, the ASR, and the military, the PAR.

Leave the Driving to Us

Unless you did your instrument training close to a military base, you've probably never flown a PAR (precision approach radar) approach. And unless you're fortunate enough to have a radar site near your home base, an ASR (airport surveillance radar) approach won't be all that familiar, either.

This lack of familiarity with radar approaches is unfortunate because if you're really in deep humus, the PAR or ASR is often the safest ticket home. After all, if you're struggling with an electrical failure, you need all the help you can get and that's exactly what radar approaches represent.

Common Ground

Both PARs and ASRs are simple enough to understand. The procedure itself consists of a qualified radar controller sitting on the ground using standard radio voice transmissions to "talk down" an aircraft on the approach. All the pilot needs is a lowly comm receiver and, yes, a handheld will do just fine. If you can hear the controller, just follow his or her instructions. Simple, neat and easy. And both the ASR and PAR can be conducted with or without a transponder.

Actually, either procedure is like being vectored for the entire approach and for my money, it's much easier to fly a vector than it is to keep the needles centered on the doughnut. Another advantage of the GCA is that you don't need an approach plate. That's because the controller will give you all the information you need for the approach, including MDAs and missed approach procedures.

On the other hand, it is nice to have *something* on paper. All NOS users get are the radar minimums in the front of the IAP booklet. In practice, however, these are only useful for finding which airports have ASR available. And that brings us to the next NOS limitation. Since PARs aren't available at civilian fields, and since civilian fields are the only ones found in NOS, you won't find anything on PAR approaches in NOS pubs.

Jeppesen, however, gives its civilian subscribers full-blown approach plates for ASRs. Military subscribers get plates for ASRs and PARs. There's no doubt about it; the Cap'n walks away with the gold on this one.

ASR Basics

There are two important things to know about the ASR. First of all, the approach is available at most (but not all) airports that have an approach control facility, as well as smaller airports located within 20 miles of a radar site. Additionally, most military fields are served by at least one ASR approach.

Of course, because they lack glideslopes, ASRs are nonpreci-sion approaches that usually have minimums roughly comparable to VOR or LOC procedures, with HATs between 300 and 400 AGL, typically.

While the ASR is actually less demanding than most other approaches, there are a few differences. If you've never flown one before, you'll immediately notice that the controller's phraseology is unusual.

The controller's handbook (Air Traffic Control, 7110.65) spells out exactly what's to be said during the approach. There may be some differences at military fields, but by and large, you'll hear the same phraseology for both the PAR and ASR.

Sometime during the early phases of the approach, but definitely before starting the final approach, the controller will inform you of the exact approach you're flying, as well as the missed approach point. Controller: "This will be a surveillance approach to runway one niner. Missed approach point is runway threshold."

If the aircraft is likely to encounter IFR conditions, the controller must issue lost comm instructions: "If no transmissions are received for one minute in the pattern or 15 seconds on final approach, attempt contact on 125.0 and proceed VFR. If unable, proceed with the ILS runway 19 approach, cross HAWKI at 2000." The term "in the pattern" means the radar pattern. It's similar to a greatly enlarged visual traffic pattern, but it includes a dogleg to final. You'll also get missed approach instructions: "Your missed approach procedure is climb to 3000, then climbing left turn to 4000, direct Albany vortac; hold west, 103 degrees inbound."

Still with me? Next comes the MDA callout. Controller: "Prepare to descend in two miles. Published minimum descent altitude two four zero."

Whoa! Maybe this standard phraseology isn't such a great idea after all. The controller's handbook is very clear about how MDAs or DHs must be given to the pilot; each digit has to be pronounced separately. But it's easy to see the potential for confusion. Someone who's unfamiliar with this type of approach could misinterpret the MDA of 240 feet (spoken "Two Four Zero") as a *heading* of 240. My advice? Always ask for confirmation when you're issued an MDA or a DH for an unfamiliar approach.

Your Own Controller

The approach commences once you've been handed off to the final controller and you've started your turn toward the runway. The final controller, by the way, usually communicates on a discrete frequency and you're his only customer so you have his undivided attention.

Expect the final controller to greet you with a radio check: "Piper Six One Alpha, Podunk approach final controller. How do you hear me?" Once you've responded that comm is loud and clear, the controller will request that you not acknowledge any further transmissions. That means exactly what it says. It would take up too much air time and you'd risk blocking the controller's instructions.

You can expect to intercept the final approach course at about a 30-degree angle (that's the dogleg from the base leg mentioned earlier). Next you'll be given a turn onto final, followed by minor heading changes to keep you aligned with the course. The controller will keep you constantly apprised of your position. Controller: "Going right of course, turn left heading 182." That's right, you'll be expected to fly right down to the degree. Next, you might hear something like this: "Slightly right of course and correcting, turn right heading 185." And later: "Turn right heading 187, on course."

Although there's no glideslope on the ASR, there's something almost as good, providing you ask for it. The controller's handbook says controllers may "provide recommended altitudes on final if the pilot requests." Like other aspects of instrument flying, good deals are available for those savvy enough to ask. These recommended altitudes will be given every mile.

If you've requested recommended altitudes, the litany from the controller should go something like this: "Recommended altitudes will be provided for each mile on final to minimum descent altitude," followed by "three miles from runway, altitude should be 1,300 feet." As long as you're at or below those recommended altitudes, you'll know that your descent rate is adequate to get you to the MDA prior to the MAP. The controller will hold your hand right to the MAP, at which point you'll be instructed to execute the missed if the runway or approach lights aren't in sight.

The PAR

If the ASR can be likened to a vectored VOR approach, then the PAR is the radar equivalent of the ILS; it's a precision approach that comes complete with course and descent guidance. The hardware itself actually consists of two radar displays—one for the course and one for descent.

Many bases now have an advanced model of the PAR called the GPN-22. Unlike the older FPN-61, the new system allows the controller to "lock onto" the aircraft shooting the approach. A dotted line on the scope shows target history. The aircraft symbol moves from right to left, and the vertical lines on the scope are one mile range ticks (darker lines are at five mile intervals). Although the screen shows the last part of the approach as a curved line, it's just an anomaly of the depiction. In reality, the course and glidepath are straight.

One note on PAR limitations: Since the PAR equipment is incapable of using transponder replies, it relies strictly on primary radar. Therefore, precipitation on final can render the approach useless. Although the new system with its moving target indicator (MTI) capability isn't as sensitive to precip on final, you usually won't know which system you're dealing with. Just realize that the PAR may be unavailable if there's a lot of rain around.

A PAR is an absolute joy to fly. A good controller can bring you right down to the numbers every time. In fact, believe it or not the approach is so accurate that decision heights are typically 100 feet AGL—the same as a CAT II ILS.

They Shoot Civilians, Don't They?

But, wait, aren't civilian pilots forbidden from using military airbases? What good is PAR if most of us can't use it?

I know a lot of pilots who would never consider landing at a military airfield, even in an emergency. These are the same folks who would decline to declare an emergency because they're afraid of the mythical and practically nonexistent "paperwork."

My advice is that if you have to land at a military base, go for it. Having dealt with quite a few civilian aircraft who have put into Air Force bases, I can tell you it's no big deal.

You'll probably be met by a follow-me truck and led to a tie down spot. Yes, they might ask you to sign a release promising not to sue the government, and they might ask for a sentence or two of explanation so they'll have something to show the CO in the morning, but that's usually the extent of it. We haven't shot anyone since last year. What with the budget crunch, it's too hard to get replacement ammo. (Just kidding. It's been two years since we shot someone.)

I've only heard of one pilot who was given a hard time for landing at an Air Force base but trust me, he really deserved it. If you need to land and want a military PAR, declare an emergency and ask for the approach. When you land, just be courteous and don't be in a hurry. You'll be surprised at how accommodating the nice men in the blue suits will be.

No-Gyro Option

The controller's patter is similar to what you'd hear during an ASR, with the addition of glideslope information wickered in with the course guidance: "Slightly right of course and holding, turn left heading 187, on glidepath."

Just as there are degrees of being off course, there are degrees of divergence from the glideslope. You might be told that you're above or below the glideslope, slightly above or below, or well above or below. This will usually be followed by trend information such as "going further above/below the glidepath," or the terms "and holding" or "and correcting."

Putting it all together, the PAR chant goes like this: "On course, on glideslope; going slightly left of course, turn right heading 192. Going slightly below the glidepath, 192 the heading, correcting to course, going further below the glidepath" and so on.

This will continue right down to decision height at which point the controller will make the call, appropriately enough, "at decision height."

If your gyros have gone south as a result of a vacuum failure, you can request a no-gyro approach for either the ASR or the PAR. Instead of issuing headings, the controller tells you to, "turn left/right," followed by the words "stop turn." All you need do is make a standard rate turn in the appropriate direction, and roll out when told to. This is a real no-brainer, but there's one catch: On final, you're expected to make half-standard rate turns.

Were I faced with a partial panel approach in low-IMC, I'd definitely go for the no-gryo option, assuming, of course, that I couldn't find an airport with acceptable VFR conditions.

Getting Some Practice

Since FAA controllers are required to conduct three ASRs per quarter (one of which must be no-gyro), they're usually pretty accommodating when you request a practice ASR. But, as with any other practice approach, your chances of success will vary inversely to the amount of traffic in the area. Pick a relatively slow time, say early morning or late evening, off the departure and arrival pushes.

Only one civil field, Troy, Alabama, has PAR, but they're still quite common in the Air Force. Just because it's a military approach, doesn't mean you can't practice one. Keep in mind, though, the base may be too busy to accommodate you or it may restrict civilian use of the PAR but it's worth asking about, nonetheless.

I'd suggest phoning the base operator at whichever facility you're planning to use and ask for the control tower number. If all else fails, ask for the number of the Public Affairs Officer and go from there. Once you get in touch with the controllers, ask for the particulars on shooting a few practice approaches. They should be happy to provide you with the information.

When It's For Real

Most of us think of a PAR or ASR an emergency procedure but there are other less trying circumstances when a GCA would be the best choice.

I know of several pilots who have had unreliable localizer or glideslope indications and, just to be sure, asked for an ASR *monitored* approach. In this case, you shoot a regular approach, ATC keeps an eye on you with ASR. It's a nice safety feature.

In the case of an alternator or generator failure you'll want to conserve as much battery power as possible. All you need for an ASR or a PAR is a comm receiver, whose power draw is the lowest of all the avionics. This is the strategy I followed on a particularly trying flight a few years back.

I was on a long cross country from Florida to Illinois with a student. We had had a rough time of it, with turbulence in Alabama and later, an alternator failure whose repair put us behind schedule and into Springfield well after dark. As if the trip wasn't amusing enough, we encountered ice.

By the time we arrived, the tower was closed so there would be no vectors to final; we'd have to shoot the full approach. Kansas City Center terminated radar service, gave us a frequency change and wished us a good night. Yeah, right.

We were cleared to the LOM, but the ADF wasn't locking on, the localizer needle wasn't anywhere close and the loran didn't agree with anything. I decided it was time to cry Uncle. I turned towards the field and started a climb to the minimum sector altitude (MSA) while switching back to Kansas City's frequency.

After what seemed like an eternity, Kansas City answered my calls and asked my intentions. By this time I was confused, tired, and stressed. "I'd like to go to the closest airport that has good weather and an ASR." And with that, we were on our way to Peoria.

That's when we had our second encounter with icing. A little later, I heard a distressed voice in my headset: "Ross, we don't have any airspeed."

Pitot heat! For as long as I'd been flying in Florida, pitot heat had been nothing more than an extra switch on the panel. I flicked it on and the ammeter showed the extra load. In a moment, the airspeed was alive and well.

The voice of the Peoria approach controller was sweet music indeed. The headings were easy to follow and we broke out before reaching MDA. Half way through the landing roll it started to snow, but I didn't care. Madeline, my instrument student, wanted to know if all IFR flights were as much fun as this one had been. I just smiled a very tired, but awfully relieved smile.

The story has a continuing happy ending. Madeline later went on to marry a close friend of mine and they now own an Aztec, which they never fly on instruments. There's a lesson there somewhere.

• Section Three •

The End of the Approach

Circling Approaches

Okay, you've completed the approach (precision or non-precision) and reached the MAP. Now it's time to either land or leave, depending on whether you see the airport or not. This section deals with what happens after you make that decision.

Landing from a straight-in approach is simple: You are already lined up with the runway, and your aircraft is already in landing configuration. But a circle-to-land approach is another matter entirely. When the weather's bad, this can be a really hair-raising experience.

The Demanding Approach

A circling approach is undoubtedly the most high-risk procedure in the books. When flown at an uncontrolled airport, especially at night, it requires a high level of proficiency in aircraft control, planning and execution.

A straight-in procedure usually has circling minimums to accommodate operations to other runways, especially when none of the other runways have straight-in approaches. Naturally, circling minimums will be higher than straight-in to provide a margin of safety while you maneuver to another runway.

There have been a number of accidents that were caused by pilots becoming disoriented after initiating the circling maneuver. It's a bad place to be: confused, slow, and close to the ground in bad weather.

Protected Areas

The tough situation is worsened by the way circling approaches are designed. As with all approach segments, there is an area of protected airspace associated with the circling approach, and it's of adequate size to make sure you've got obstacle clearance while you crank the old bird around for landing. The bad news is that the clearance isn't a whole lot, and there's no room for error: there might be a tower, hillside, or whatever lurking just beyond the edge of the protected area, one that's higher than the MDA. This doesn't leave any room for error or poor altitude control.

Be suspicious if the airport has a circling procedure only. It almost always indicates that there are obstacles or terrain which prevented the FAA from designing a straight-in procedure. In these cases, a circling procedure is established so the airport will have some instrument approach capability. These approaches can be safely conducted, but review the procedure carefully to determine if you'll have to fly like a champion aerobatic pilot to maneuver to the landing runway.

Remember, when the final approach course of a procedure isn't aligned within 30 degrees of any runway, circling minimums apply. These minimums will be higher than those for a straight-in and provide at least 300 feet of obstacle clearance inside the circling area.

The circling approach area, or protected area, is established by drawing arcs with radii that extend from each runway threshold. The radii of the arcs depend on the approach speed of the aircraft (approach category). Each category has a larger arc associated with it, so the faster you are, the more room you have to maneuver. They range from a radius of 1.3 nm for Category A (1.3 Vso < 91 kts) to 2.3 nm for Category D (1.3 Vso >141 kts). There is a Category E, but it's for military aircraft with very high stall speeds—1.3 Vso greater than 166 kts.

Naturally, the larger the protected area the greater the chance that an obstacle will poke up into the floor of it, which is what usually forces higher minimums for higher-category operations. Again, the minimums always provide at least 300 feet of clearance. The upshot of this is that higher-category aircraft may be prohibited from using the procedure at all (see, there really *are* some advantages to not flying a Learjet).

The category (and therefore the protected area size and applicable minimums) is based on an approach speed of 1.3 Vso at maximum gross landing weight. However, that's just a reference point. If you *choose* to fly faster, you must obey the minima for the higher category even if you can technically fit into the lower one. For example, if your airplane normally fits Category A, but you elect to fly the approach at a speed that places you in Category C, you must adhere to Category C minimums. This is because the size of the protected area takes into account the larger turning radii of faster aircraft. Since an unusually high speed can take you out of the obstacle clearance area, your actual circling speed is what must be used to determine your minimums.

You can get a clue as to how flat the terrain around the airport is by comparing the minimums for the various categories. The horizontal size of the protected area is determined by aircraft speed, and its floor is determined by obstacle clearance requirements. If the minimums for Category D are the same as Category A, you know that there's nothing out there to run into. If you see a sudden jump in MDA, there's a reason for it.

The obvious question is, how do you know if you're getting close to the edge of the protected area? Well, you don't. You could probably use distance from a loran or GPS waypoint at the middle of the airport for reference, but your workload is high enough already without having to worry about exactly where the edge of the protected area is. Rest assured that it's plenty big enough to keep you out of trouble as long as you respect the speed limitations and keep it in relatively tight.

What happens if you lose sight of the airport during the circling maneuver? If you turn the wrong way, you'll run past the edge of the protected area pretty quickly, and then all bets are off. Should you re-enter the clouds during the circling maneuver, turn towards the airport, climb immediately, then get established on the missed approach course. Remember, normally the protected area extends at least 1.3 miles (Category A minimums) beyond the far edge of the airport's runways, which is plenty of room to get up and out of trouble. After you get a positive rate of climb, you can sort out the missed approach procedure.

There are exceptions to the rule, however. At some airports, obstructions can alter the usual size and shape of the protected area. This will be noted on the plate. Make sure you note these remarks and remain aware of where you are relative to the hazards.

MAP at Threshold

Refer to the NDB-A approach for Arcata, California on the following pages. This approach may seem appealing at first since no timing is necessary; just fly a typical non-precision procedure until you see the field or cross the NDB. Notice that the NDB is close to the threshold of Runway 32.

Don't attempt a circling maneuver if you do not see the field until just before crossing the NDB. At this point, you'll be close to the runway threshold at 800 feet agl and at a 60-degree angle to Runway 14-32. Steep maneuvering will be necessary for Runways 14 or 02 and a landing on Runway 32 should not be considered.

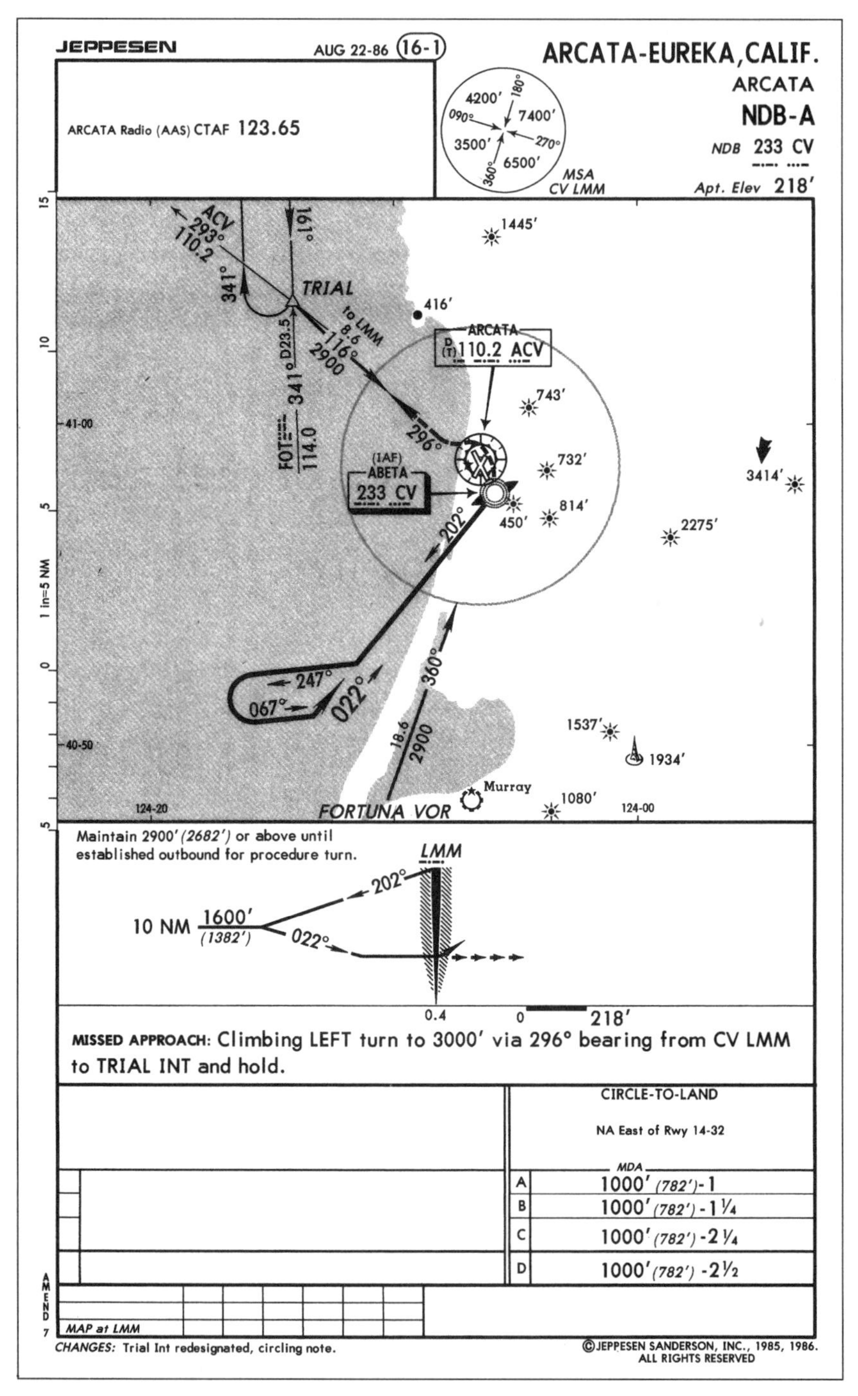
JEPPESEN
AUG 22-86 (16-1)
ARCATA-EUREKA,CALIF.
ARCATA
NDB-A
NDB 233 CV
Apt. Elev 218'
ARCATA Radio (AAS) CTAF 123.65
4200'
7400'
3500'
6500'
MSA
CV LMM
1445'
416'
743'
732'
814'
450'
2275'
3414'
1537'
1934'
1080'
ACV
293°
110.2
161°
341°
TRIAL
to LMM
8.6
116°
2900
D23.5
341°
FOT
114.0
ARCATA
110.2 ACV
296°
(IAF)
ABETA
233 CV
202°
247°
067°
022°
360°
18.6
2900
Murray
FORTUNA VOR
41-00
40-50
124-20
124-00
1 in=5 NM
Maintain 2900' (2682') or above until established outbound for procedure turn.
LMM
202°
10 NM 1600' (1382')
022°
0.4
0
218'
MISSED APPROACH: Climbing LEFT turn to 3000' via 296° bearing from CV LMM to TRIAL INT and hold.
CIRCLE-TO-LAND
NA East of Rwy 14-32
MDA
A 1000' (782')-1
B 1000' (782')-1 1/4
C 1000' (782')-2 1/4
D 1000' (782')-2 1/2
MAP at LMM
AMEND 7
CHANGES: Trial Int redesignated, circling note.
©JEPPESEN SANDERSON, INC., 1985, 1986. ALL RIGHTS RESERVED

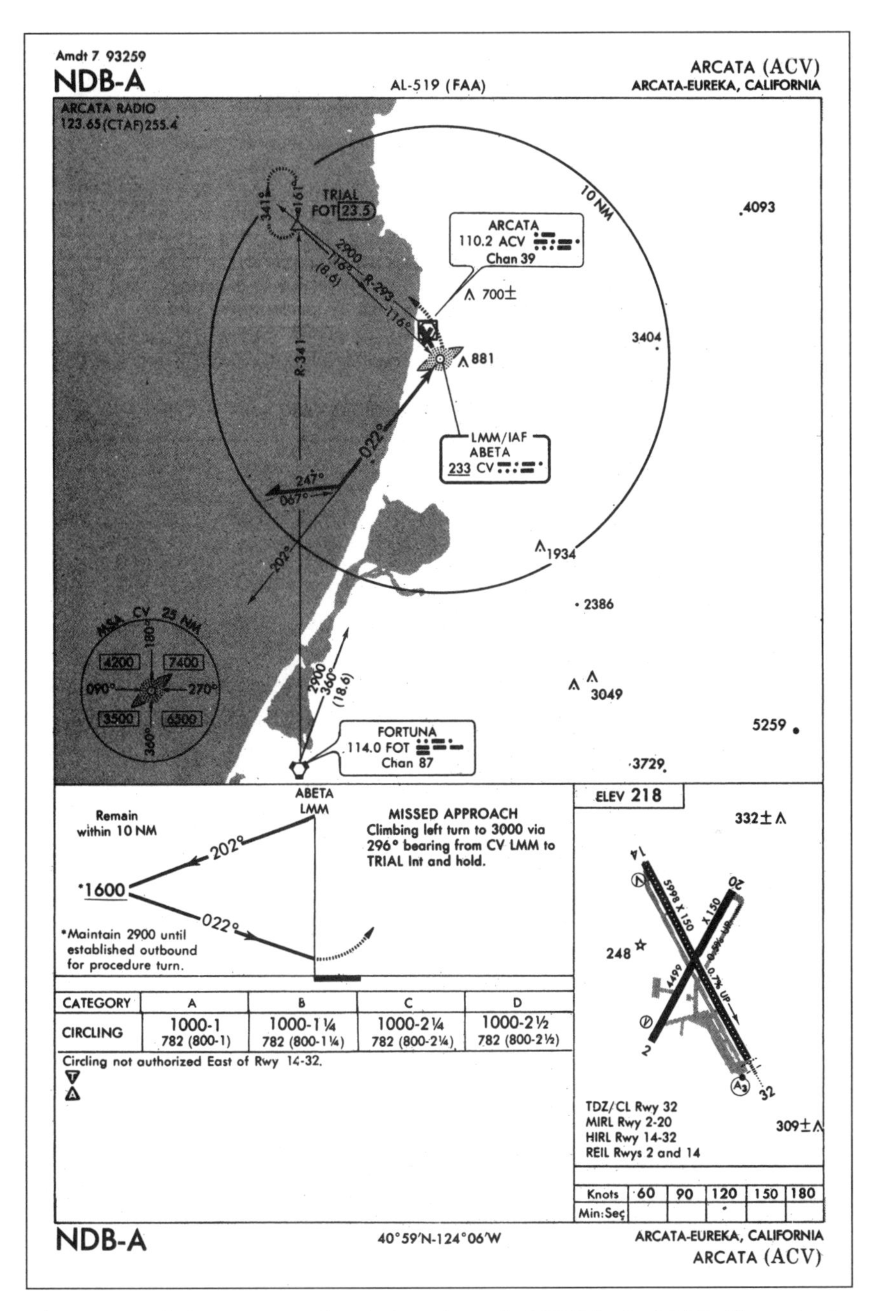

This approach does not require timing since the NDB is the MAP. If you don't see the runway until close to the NDB, you'll be over the threshold of 32 at 800 ft agl and at a 60-degree angle to the runway.

Circling is not authorized east of Runway 14-32, so Runway 20 is not usable during this procedure. Assuming you see the field in time, you could enter a left base for Runway 32, a right downwind for Runway 14 or a modified right base to final for Runway 02.

If a missed approach is necessary, a turn toward the center of the airport will keep you clear of obstacles until established on the missed approach track, which is the 296 magnetic bearing from the NDB. That could be tricky if you missed the approach while circling to Runway 02. It won't hurt to begin your climb immediately.

Category D aircraft can use this procedure with the same minimums as Category A, so you know the circling approach area has a radius of 2.3 nm. This provides a good safety margin when flying a Category A or B aircraft, provided you remain within the speed for those categories. The prohibition against circling east of Runway 14-32 is probably due to the fact that adequate obstacle clearance cannot be provided in that area. Don't assume you can sneak into this area in a Category A, B or C aircraft. You don't know exactly where the obstacles are relative to your position, even though they're charted. Strict adherence to the limitations on the chart will keep you out of trouble.

Vertical guidance during a circling maneuver can be troublesome, especially at night. At this airport, Runways 14 and 02 each have a VASI which should be an integral part of a circling maneuver. A missed approach should be strongly considered if you lose sight of the VASI after turning final.

Odd Restriction

The VOR-A approach to Meeker, Colorado on pages 134-135 has an interesting restriction. The final approach course guides you in northwest of the runway, but notice that circling is prohibited in this area! All circling must be conducted southeast of the field.

When flying this procedure, you should cross the runway at the MDA. Doing so places you over the field at almost 1100 feet agl. You can enter a normal downwind from this point and be sure to keep it in sight at all times. The runway length is 4500 feet and neither end has a VASI.

In the event a missed approach is necessary, an initial climbing turn toward the runway will keep you safe until established on the EKR R-113, the first part of the missed approach track.

Good planning is a must for this procedure. Review the profile section of the chart. The final approach segment is only 2.1 nm. You must descend 840 feet to the MDA after crossing the VOR. At 90 knots, the time to the MAP is one minute and twenty-four seconds. This might not appear to be a large amount of altitude to lose, unless you want to arrive at the MDA before reaching the MAP. A descent rate of about 1000 fpm is needed to arrive at the MDA thirty seconds prior to the MAP.

Timing is Important

For the Arcata approach, timing is not needed because the navaid is practically on the field. That's not always the case, though, and using the stopwatch can be critical to locating the MAP.

Many pilots neglect to note the time when passing the final approach fix. The circling approach is even more dangerous if you're uncertain about the location of the missed approach point. Unless a VOR or NDB is on the airport, or DME fixes are available, this is courting disaster when obstructions are in the vicinity. Get in the habit of always timing the approach, so you'll know precisely when to start the missed approach in the event the airport and/or runway environment aren't in sight.

If no radar is available, you could be asked to report your position. The answer depends on your positional awareness and timing passing the FAF.

An ILS should be timed passing the non-precision FAF (Maltese cross). This guarantees positional awareness if the glideslope fails and you need to continue with a localizer-only approach. The FAF for an ILS is the point you intercept the glideslope at the designated altitude on the chart.

Plan Missed Approach

The possibility of a missed approach should be carefully planned before beginning the procedure. Know the direction in which you will turn and where the missed approach procedure starts.

The VOR-A procedure at El Monte, California (page 137) is a good example. Circling is authorized from any point, but the safest maneuver is to cross the field at MDA and enter downwind for the landing runway. The lowest MDA is 780 feet (484 feet agl) and there is an obstacle at 444 feet msl on the southwest corner of the field.

A missed approach while on downwind for either runway should begin with a turn toward the landing runway before following the missed approach procedure, which in this case requires a climb to 1000 feet on a 270 heading. After reaching 1000 feet, you should climb to 4000 feet while turning left to intercept the PDZ VOR R-246, which is a different VOR than the one used to fly the approach. Your radios should be set ahead, just in case. Having DME is a definite plus when flying this procedure.

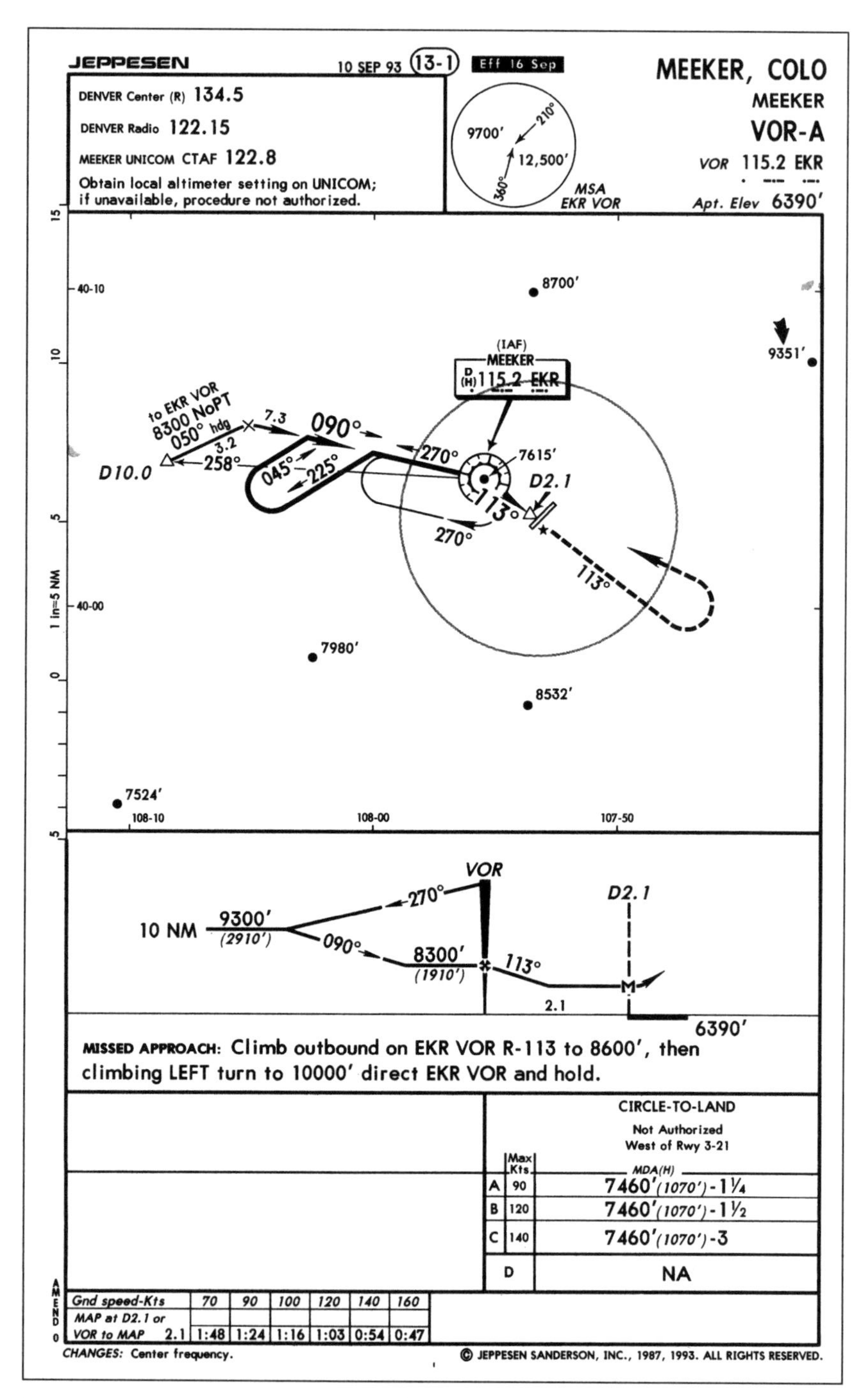

Gnd speed-Kts	70	90	100	120	140	160
MAP at D2.1 or VOR to MAP 2.1	1:48	1:24	1:16	1:03	0:54	0:47

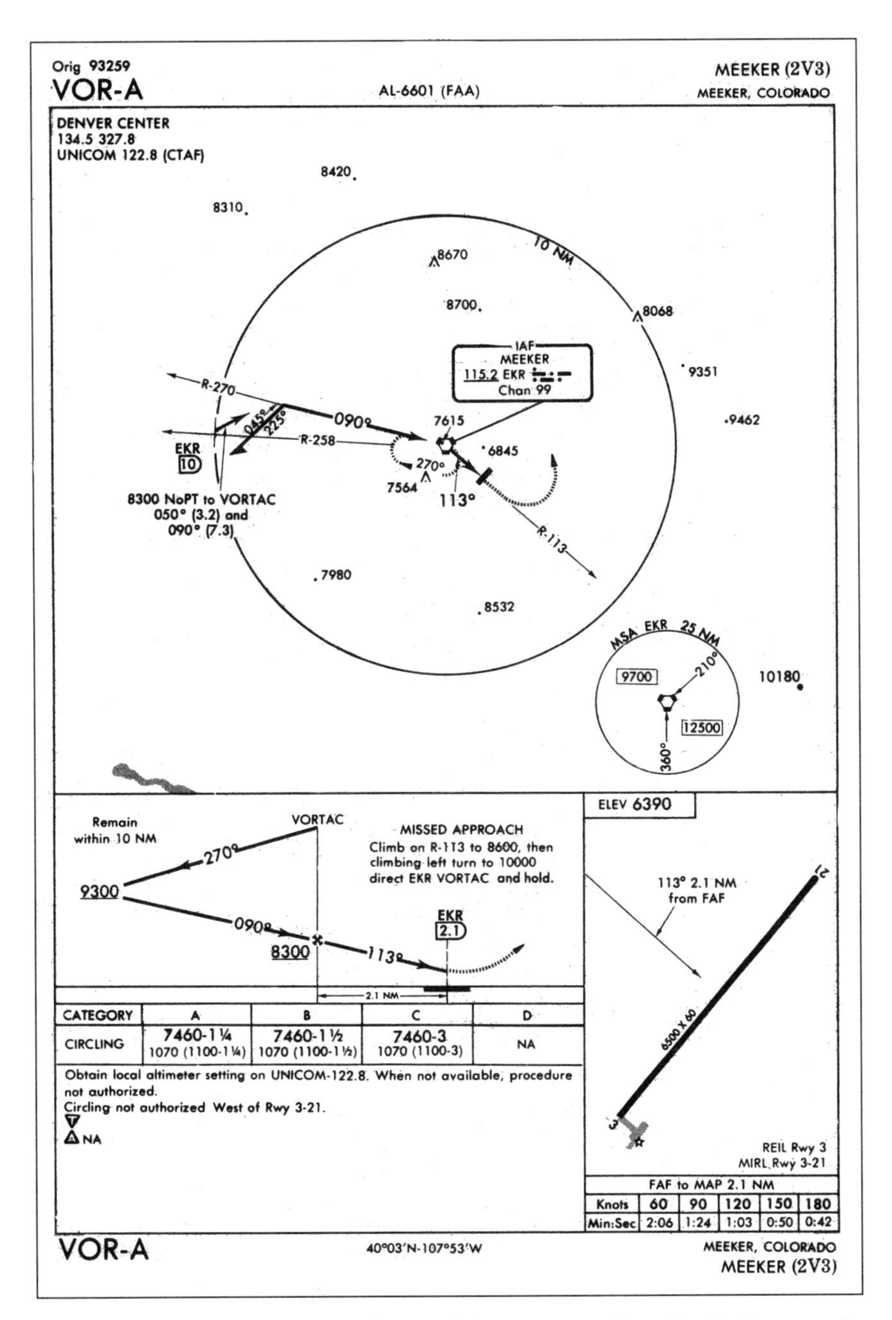

Note that circling is not allowed west of the runway, where the final approach course is located. Also note that Category D aircraft may not use the procedure due to obstacles that would interfere with the protected area.

Basic maneuvers

Suppose you arrive at the MDA and can't land straight-in. You're close to cloud bases, with reduced visibility due to rain, snow, fog, etc. This is where pilot technique reverts back to your student pilot days when you were taught ground reference maneuvers, dividing your attention between the instruments and outside references controlling attitude, airspeed and altitude. You must bring these skills together to set up a final approach to landing.

Circling approaches in low visibility and/or strong wind are prime opportunities for stall/spin accidents. Never bank more than 30 degrees in the pattern, even to regain sight of the runway or avoid a cloud. Pay close attention to airspeed. Overbanking and slowing during a loss of visual reference can simultaneously bring on a stall and disorientation . If you can't make the runway with standard maneuvers, accept the situation and initiate a missed approach.

Circling approaches can be fraught with hazards, so prepare for the worst in advance and be spring-loaded for a missed approach. Remember, the airport will still be there when you return under more favorable circumstances.

The End Game

Here are a few low-visibility close-in techniques you can use to position yourself to land from circling approaches. Remember, there could be other traffic in the pattern, so a determined outside watch is mandatory. Don't rely on unicom for complete traffic information. There could be no-radio aircraft operating or someone not monitoring the frequency.

The FAA *Instrument Flying Handbook* presents four options for circling approaches. Two which are useful if you see the runway in time are: 1) putting yourself on a base leg (if approaching upwind) or 2) sidestepping to a downwind leg (if approaching downwind). The other two are used if you see the airport at the last minute and are aligned with the runway. If approaching upwind, you overfly the runway and enter a normal traffic pattern. If downwind, you fly over the runway, reverse course and fly an upwind leg, then a crosswind to a normal downwind leg. Of course, the patterns should be kept tighter and (probably) lower then they would be for VFR operations.

There are two more options you can use if the runway isn't aligned with the final approach course and you need to fly directly over the airport before making your approach (in other words, if you're making the approach downwind and the runways are not aligned with the final approach course).

In the first, you would fly to the center of the airport and turn towards

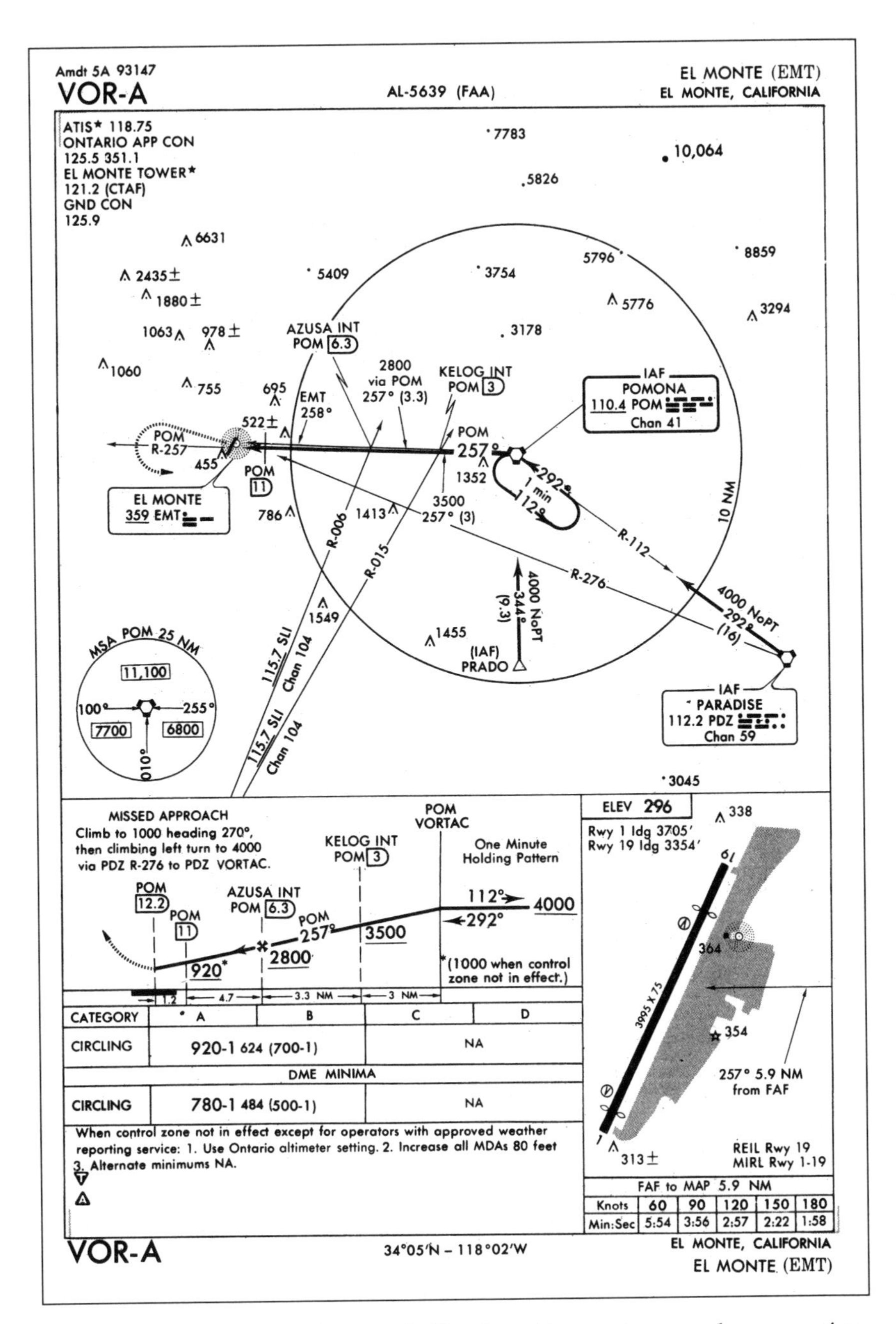

While there are no restrictions on circling here, the safest move when executing the missed approach is a turn back towards the runway.

the approach end of the landing runway, flying along the runway centerline. On reaching the end, enter a standard rate 90-degree turn to the right. At the 90-degree point, immediately roll into a 270-degree turn to the left, rolling out on the runway heading.

You could use a 90-left/270-right if conditions require; however, if possible the turns should be made in the direction that gives the pilot in command the best view of the runway during the turns.

In the other option you essentially fly a normal traffic pattern. As you come up over the airport enter a normal downwind, and fly base and final approach legs. Keep it tight enough to maintain contact with the airport (within reason...no steep turns, please).

With all options, you must maintain at least the circling altitude until final descent for landing. As in every landing, before-landing checklists must be accomplished before final descent. The 90/270 described above is a course reversal, which is a handy way of making procedure turns, as long as a teardrop procedure isn't depicted on the chart.

Think It Out in Advance

Flying a circling approach is tough, no doubt about it. It really pays to study the plates beforehand and think through the entire approach.

You should be heads-up and ready to act when it's time to initiate the circling maneuver; the last second is no time to collect yourself and ruminate over how you'll fly the last segment of this approach.

Missed Approaches

Missed approaches in the real world are actually quite rare; we usually end up landing at our intended destination on the first try. Rare or not, though, the miss is something that an instrument pilot needs to keep well-honed.

The reason is simple: The MAP and its immediate vicinity are dangerous places to be if you can't see anything. Consider that on an ILS you're descending at 500 feet per minute or so, only 200 feet above the ground. If you retain that nice, gentle descent rate you'll smack the pavement a mere 24 seconds after reaching the MAP. Add to this the need to get your airplane established in a climb and cleaned up, plus navigate your way out of there, and it's easy to see why missed approaches deserve careful study.

In this chapter we'll take a couple of different looks at the missed approach and various aspects of it. First is an overview of missed approaches and planning for them.

Abandoning the Approach

Accepting the obligation to fly a missed approach is analogous to punting on fourth-and-15 with the ball on your own 20—with one exception: Not punting is dumb; not flying the miss when you don't have minimums is both dumb and highly illegal. In fact, it can be odds-on lethal, as many an accident has shown.

Why some pilots elect to duck under the DH or the MDA at the approach point either for "a look" or determined to bull their way through to the runway is a painful puzzle. An aversion to inconvenience, arrogant overconfidence, uncertainty over what to do during the miss and after—these and other, similar excuses may lie behind such decisions, but considering the risks, they make no sense.

A miss can definitely be inconvenient, but as much as death or injury? Nevertheless, like lost yardage and fourth-down punts, misses come with the IFR game, with the consolation that they are made necessary by acts of nature and not by the failure of your offensive linemen.

If arrogant superconfidence is part of your mentality you'd better find a safer game. If you blindly grope for the ground, the percentages are you'll find it, where it can bend you for good. That's why the regs say you can't try it.

Part of the Plan

Uncertainty over handling the missed approach and then coming up with a reasonable intention afterward is an unnecessary burden to carry. A punt isn't the end of the game, it's merely a maneuver that leads to further decisions that should already be part of the overall plan—just like the missed approach. From the beginning of your flight planning, the possibility of a miss at your destination should be part of your strategy if the weather briefing indicates that minimums could be jeopardized. Listen, read and plan.

Listen to or read the forecasts for your destination. If you won't have at least a 2,000-foot ceiling and 3 miles visibility from an hour before your ETA to an hour after, you must file an alternate. Your filed choice of alternate isn't binding if you want to notify ATC of a change, but it's important not only if you lose communications but in helping you to plan in terms of expected conditions. Your plan may change as you update the weather during the flight, but at least you'll have something to work from as the situation forms.

Executing the post-miss plan is actually part three of the missed approach procedure. Part one entails preparation for the miss well before you reach the MAP. Part two is the flight from the DH or MAP to the published hold. Part three is deciding what you will do next; try again immediately, wait a bit or go for the alternate.

Preparing for the Miss

If the possibility exists, begin by assuming you'll have to fly it, no matter what you haven't had to since getting your ticket. This time, the field may go down during the approach. This time, for once you may screw up the approach beyond saving it. This time, for some reason, ATC may request that you miss. All unlikely, sure, but ready yourself mentally (and, yes, emotionally).

The goal at the MAP is to clear the terrain as expeditiously as possible, including radio towers and other objects that might be poking into the overcast, where you could be. For example, take the ILS Runway 5 approach at Greater Buffalo International (pp 142-143).

On this approach, the DH is 906 feet and the circle-to-land MDA is 1,180. Just off the northeast end of Runway 5 is an 835-foot tower, and just to the right of the departure end is an 862-foot-high tank. The design of the missed approach path is, first, to put you above and past those obstructions and then take you to the hold.

Therefore, the procedure dictates a "climb to 1,200′, then climbing RIGHT turn to 6000′ via heading 090°...."

There's more to the procedure than that, but if (think *when*) you reach the DH and, as the AIM says, "visual reference to the runway environment is insufficient to complete the landing," *that* is what you need to know as well as you know your name. In fact, you can afford to forget your name but not the procedure.

The single most important thing about any missed approach procedure is the first word: *Climb*. On an ILS you're pretty darned close to the ground at DH, descending, and with the airplane in landing configuration. You must get away from the ground immediately if you execute the missed.

At the DH or MAP, immediately and simultaneously raise the nose and apply climb power, then check the VSI for a positive rate of climb and the airspeed indicator to make sure you have climb airspeed. Then scan back to the attitude indicator for wings-level (not turn) flight.

With the climb safely established, clean up the aircraft. In most airplanes, if you have flown the approach with gear down and an approach flap setting, raise the gear, then the flaps. There are certain exceptions to this procedure, however, so check the Pilot's Operating Handbook.

Retaining Safeguards

Reaching 1,200 feet should take no time at all, so be prepared to turn right to 090° to climb "between" the tower and tank; you should have adequate vertical clearance by now, but every bit of safeguard counts.

Note that your concentration is on climbing and flying proper headings based on your scan of the panel. Don't look down at the approach plate, don't fiddle with the radio to report the miss, don't twiddle with the OBS. Fly the airplane; you'll have time for the other chores shortly. Allow as little chance for spatial or mental disorientation as you can while you're still close to the ground.

As we'll see in a moment, this discipline is a product of following the classic five Ts (Turn, Time, Twist, Throttle, Talk).

The availability of the approach plate as a crutch and the obligation

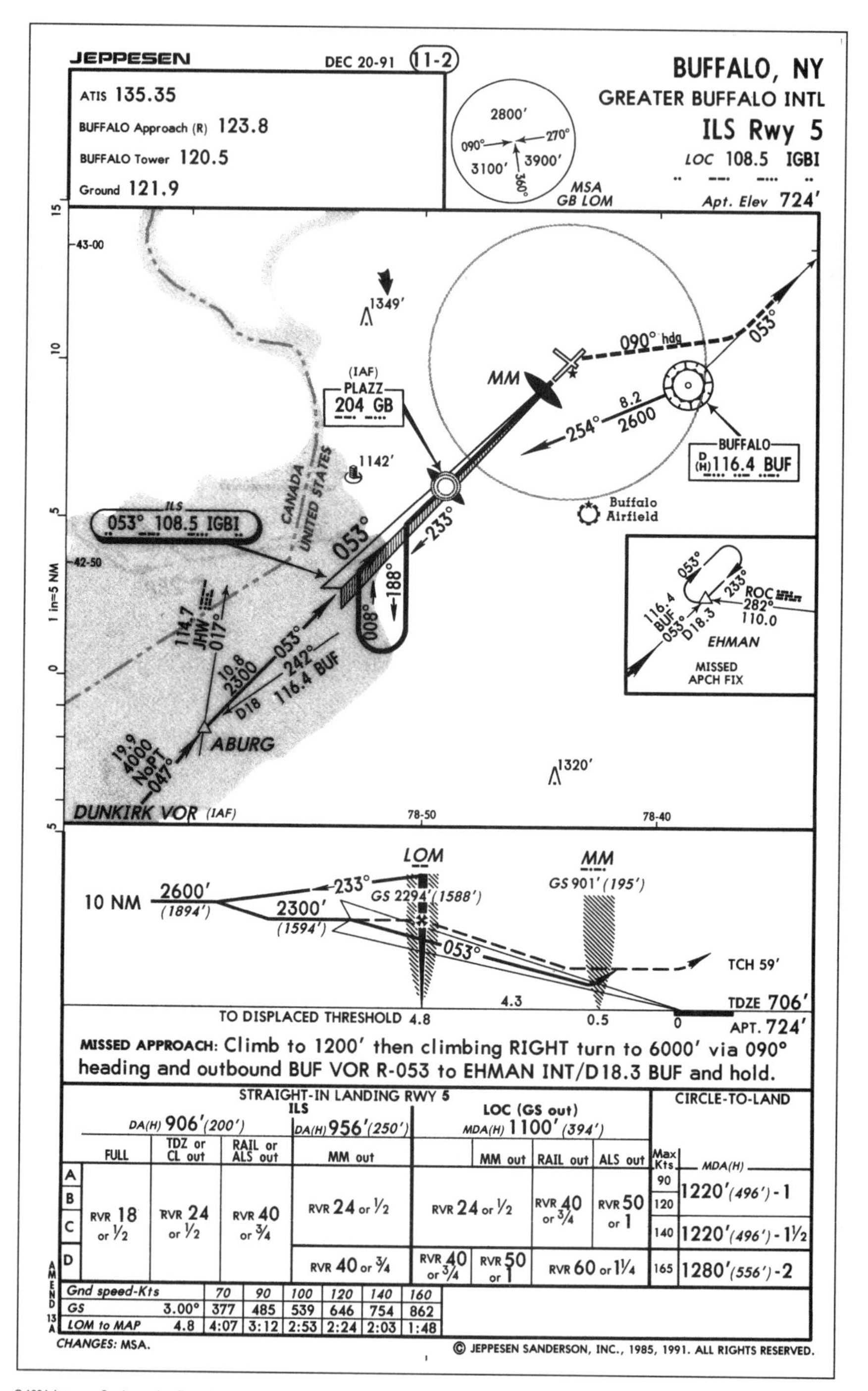

STRAIGHT-IN LANDING RWY 5

	ILS DA(H) 906'(200') FULL	ILS DA(H) 906'(200') TDZ or CL out	ILS DA(H) 906'(200') RAIL or ALS out	ILS DA(H) 956'(250') MM out	LOC (GS out) MDA(H) 1100'(394')	LOC MM out	LOC RAIL out	LOC ALS out
A, B, C	RVR 18 or ½	RVR 24 or ½	RVR 40 or ¾	RVR 24 or ½	RVR 24 or ½		RVR 40 or ¾	RVR 50 or 1
D				RVR 40 or ¾	RVR 40 or ¾	RVR 50 or 1	RVR 60 or 1¼	

CIRCLE-TO-LAND

	Max Kts	MDA(H)
A	90	1220'(496')-1
B	120	
C	140	1220'(496')-1½
D	165	1280'(556')-2

Gnd speed-Kts		70	90	100	120	140	160
GS	3.00°	377	485	539	646	754	862
LOM to MAP	4.8	4:07	3:12	2:53	2:24	2:03	1:48

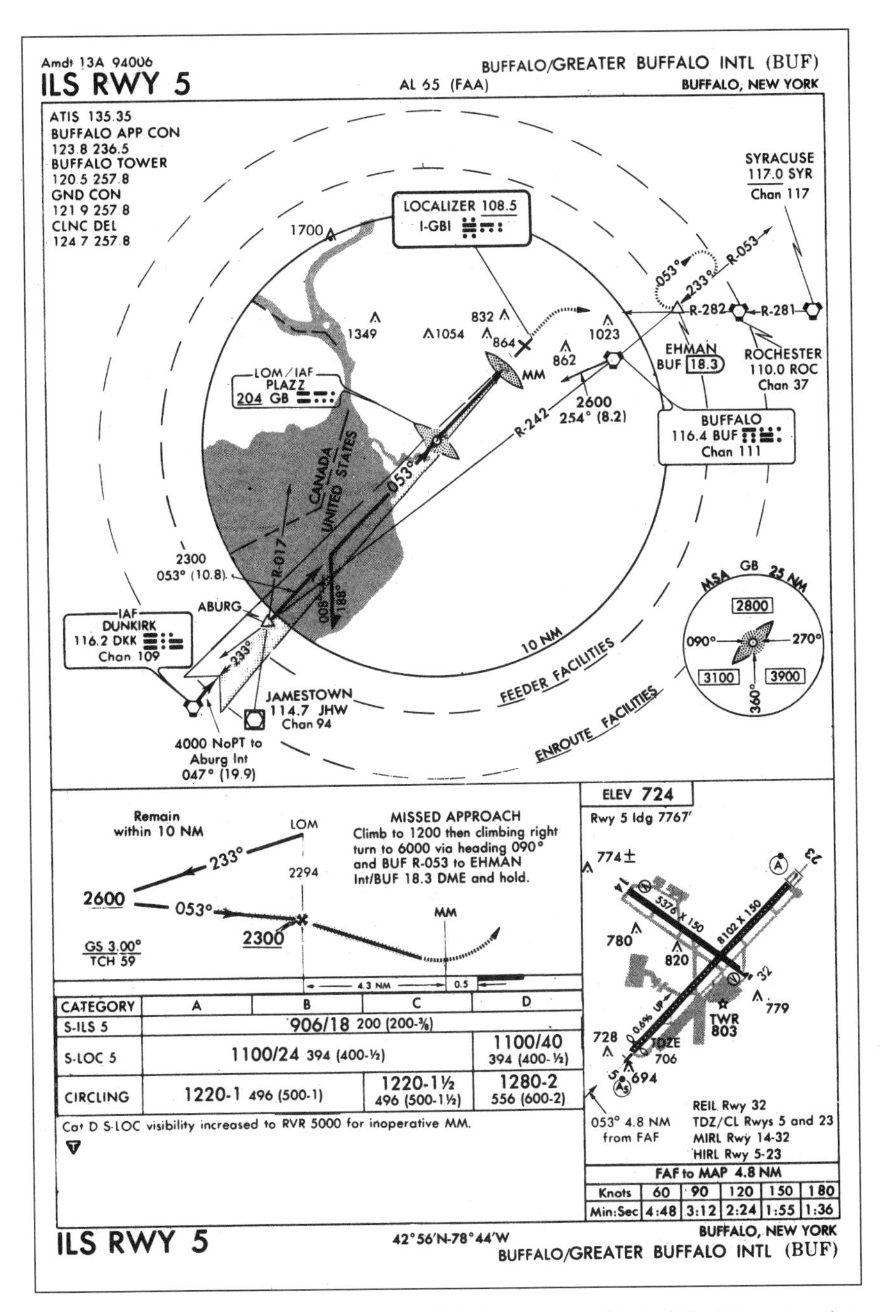

CATEGORY	A	B	C	D
S-ILS 5	906/18 200 (200-⅜)			
S-LOC 5	1100/24 394 (400-½)			1100/40 394 (400-¾)
CIRCLING	1220-1 496 (500-1)		1220-1½ 496 (500-1½)	1280-2 556 (600-2)

Cat D S-LOC visibility increased to RVR 5000 for inoperative MM.

Knots	60	90	120	150	180
Min:Sec	4:48	3:12	2:24	1:55	1:36

The missed approach procedure at Buffalo is not complicated, but there is a lot of detail to remember: two altitudes, two turns, a VOR to track outbound, and a DME distance to monitor.

to report a missed approach are powerful temptations to look away from the panel and forget your first priority in the crucial first stage of a missed approach. Just how tempting? Ask your gray-haired instructor how he got those gray hairs and he'll tell you about students who yielded to it.

Remember that Talk—reporting—is the *last* of the five Ts in sequence. ATC won't bust you for taking care of the airplane before you report.

Looking down to read the procedure is a compulsion that can (must) be fought by preparation before you actually begin the miss. Once you know which approach you'll be flying and there for which miss procedure, you can establish the vital data in your memory. During the intermediate segment, memorize—it helps to write it down in big letters, numbers and symbols—at least the beginning of the procedure: The altitude to climb to, and the turn to make (if any). Writing stimulates short-term memorization, but even if you don't write, keep things simple enough so that you won't forget or *fear* forgetting.

Fear of forgetting can cause you to consult the plate or your lap board when you neither should nor really need to. In the case of the ILS Rwy 5 procedure we've been following, all you need to know immediately is where to head on the initial climb, your target altitude and your next heading on reaching it.

The rest of the procedure can be consulted when you've accomplished those first couple of tasks (in this case, heading outbound on the Buffalo VOR R-053 to Ehman intersection and holding). Not that any of the details should surprise you; you should have looked it over at least once early on, perhaps when you first received the ATIS report indicating which approach to expect. The point is that by preparing, you won't be reduced to learning and doing everything at once and will have the life-preserving essentials at the forefront of your mind.

Setting the Headings

If, in an absolute pinch, you forget the initial path of the procedure and an early turn is involved, don't guess at the direction but climb straight ahead until you can glance at your lap board or the plate. This way, you'll remain climbing over the airport and within the protected circle-to-land area. Furthermore, if a turn is involved, be sure not to turn prematurely, which could take you into terrain or an obstruction.

As in the five Ts, the turn (or lack thereof) becomes your first priority after establishing the climb. Your *first* acts are to throttle up to climb power and raise the nose. No timing will be called for. Once you are heading upward and in the right direction, you can take care of the fine navigation by setting your OBS (if called for) and navigating as directed. This should still give you time for a prompt-enough report to ATC.

There is an exception to the rule of punctiliously following the miss procedure: If you are circling to land and lose sight of the airport. FAR 91.175 states that you must initiate a miss immediately. However, though the procedure will specify a left or right turn, if you are maneuvering to land on a different runway, the specified turn could take you the wrong way, i.e. away from the airport and the obstruction clearance area. Therefore, when circling, always begin the miss with a climbing turn towards the airport.

Aiming for the Hold

The miss procedure we've been following specifies a second turn, an intercept of the Buffalo vortac 053° radial, which will take you to Ehman intersection and the hold. Once you are established on your 090° climbing leg, you should have time to twist in the radial. Keep in mind that from due east you will turn northeastward (outbound 053°).

In fact, at first read of any miss procedure, register the basic compass directions you'll be flying. In many cases, the holding fix is at the FAF, behind you, so you can plan to turn to the opposite direction. You shouldn't need to check the plate or to center the VOR needle to figure out the heading. Just memorize it before starting final.

If the holding fix is an NDB, simply turn in the proper direction until the needle is on the nose. Where the fix is a VOR or if a specific course must be intercepted but in a shorter time than is the case at Buffalo, the appropriate heading should be noted and memorized during the intermediate segment.

As you aim for the holding pattern, you should be determining, if you haven't already, how you'll enter the hold. Entries to missed approach holds are rarely direct; the pattern usually is on the FAC on the out-bound side of the fix. In this case, while the hold is at a distance from the approach course, its position and configuration place you as approaching it along the reciprocal of the inbound course. Therefore, as you cross the fix, (Ehman intersection), you may enter via a teardrop (left to 023° and around) or a parallel (053° and reverse course) maneuver.

"What Are Your Intentions?"

ATC loves to ask that, especially if you've not the foggiest. Here's the bugaboo that, perhaps, most scares pilots as they face a missed approach. What *are* the choices after a miss?

Statistically, the favorite resolve is, "I'll go to my alternate," but is that really likely? You've probably just missed an approach in below-minimums weather that probably extends over a wide area—as was forecast. To be legal, your alternate must have been forecasting at least 600 and 2. "Chance of," "variable to," or "occasionally" anything better remains unacceptable. So, with the prevailing local conditions, where is your alternate likely to be? Far enough away to be undesirable as a destination.

In bad weather, the limiting factor on a particular trip may be the availability of a legal alternate within the range of the aircraft. This is especially so for singles of lower speed and fuel capacity.

As we've said, after the miss, "intentions" usually boil down to three types:

First, you can try again at your destination. Unless a field is mightily socked in, a second try through a ragged ceiling and variable visibility might succeed. Socks do get holes in them—while you were squinting at swirling gray out the windshield, your passenger might have spotted the approach lights out the side window. Another try—or more—could pay off.

It isn't really like passing on fourth down and 15 from your own 20. *If* you have sufficient fuel and *cool,* it's okay to shoot several approaches to the same field. But like any trustworthy coach or quarterback, be self-honest: Are you fresh? Is your judgment working soundly? Are you optimistic, pessimistic or coldly realistic? (If not the third, think again.) Do you feel truly comfortable with this choice?

How is your performance likely to be, considering how you've been doing and how you feel? When you're reaching to minimums, that's strikingly relevant.

You might try an end run by flying a different approach. A downwind landing might be necessary, but if there's a decently long runway, the view could be less oppressive at a MAP as far as three miles from the one you know so well, even with the same minimums.

Your second option is to hold in wait for improving conditions and then try the approach again. For this, have your fuel calculated to the minute, your weather briefing thorough to the nines and your knowledge of local conditions expert to the nth degree.

Alternative three is another field, either your alternate or perhaps and airport closer by where the hole in the sock is letting airplanes in. This is one of those times when ATC can provide especially warm service. Ask and you may receive better than you hoped.

Don't let the relative rarity of real missed approaches lull you, or the apparent complexity of the procedures and choices intimidate you. Approach every approach with a plan that includes a detailed consideration of how you'll handle the miss. Prior planning pays. It pays so well, in fact, that you will probably have your intentions worked out before you reach the holding fix.

So, when the weather is looking grim and you have to punt, punt. But stay on the ball: Have a game plan ready, stay legal and play the percentages.

The mere ability to fly a perfect ILS under the hood does not mean you'll automatically ace the missed approach procedure when you're in real IMC with your knuckles white and your palms sweating. Missed approaches in actual conditions can be very challenging, and mulling over the missed approach is something you should do as part of your usual self-examination before making an instrument flight.

In this section we'll look at some points to consider when evaluating your ability to handle the missed in real weather.

Preparing for the Missed

When the weather is at minimums, successfully completing an approach is challenging for a pilot who doesn't fly low approaches regularly. The first consideration when low IFR conditions exist should be how these conditions relate to your personal minimums. Many pilots establish personal minimums to avoid taking off into or landing in conditions beyond their ability. Just because you demonstrate an ILS down to minimums under the hood, doesn't mean you're comfortable doing it under actual conditions.

If you lack confidence in your ability to fly an approach to minimums, you're likely to have problems with one or more elements of it. Anxiety associated with something you fear, or have doubts about your competence to complete successfully, is enough to get the hands shakin' and knees a knockin'. Add to that something unexpected, e.g., electrical failure or no green lights on the gear, and you have the potential for an accident.

Anxiety Produces Doubt

If you're anxious about your ability to complete the approach, you probably won't remember the missed approach procedure either. If you reach DH, knowing you're close to the ground and can't see it, then suddenly realize you forgot the missed approach procedure, what will you do? You'll look at the approach chart. Meanwhile, the airplane could descend into the ground.

Time is critical when you're close to the ground and faced with a missed approach. If you descend at 500 feet per minute, it takes 24 seconds to reach the surface from a DH of 200 feet agl. If you look down at the approach chart for the missed approach procedure, your rate of descent could increase.

Approach light towers or other obstacles could be higher than the end of the runway. It wouldn't take long to hit something if you didn't immediately execute the missed approach at DH. The smart thing to do if you forget the missed approach procedure is to add full power and climb. However, you still must divert your attention from reconfiguring the airplane to figure out where you need to go.

Know before you go

You shouldn't be there in the first place if the weather is below what you know you can handle. If you do your homework before the flight, you'll have good alternates along the route and for your destination in case the weather isn't what you expected.

Good alternates should be high on the priority list when you check weather. The last thing you want is to be forced to fly an approach you normally would consider below your personal minimums or ability to complete. Your confidence level or lack of it directly affects the outcome.

The approach to minimums, followed by the missed approach, are probably the most difficult maneuvers you'll face in your flying career. It's demanding since the airplane is configured for landing during the approach. In a very short period, you must decide whether to land or make the missed approach.

You must be aware of everything going on around you. Is the attitude where you want it? Is the bank angle correct? Is the aircraft climbing? Did the engines respond to full power? Did the gear and flaps properly retract? Are the radios set for the missed approach fix? These are heavy tasks for any pilot and harder still for one who isn't sharp.

Study it First

How do you prepare for the missed approach? Understanding the missed approach procedure comes first. This procedure provides a safe routing for an airplane close to the ground while it climbs to an altitude where you're assured of remaining clear of the surrounding terrain. Following a published missed approach procedure usually leads to a holding pattern at a nearby fix. Chances are you won't hold unless you're in a non-radar environment or there are others waiting to make the same approach.

Then Practice

Prepare for a missed approach through practice. Since we don't often miss an approach, your personal minimums should include at least one missed approach a month. Practicing the missed approach gives you a good feel for timing when the real one occurs. You'll also be more familiar with the steps in reconfiguring the aircraft from the approach to a climb. The more complex the airplane, the higher the workload and a single pilot will be busy. If you haven't done a missed approach recently, you can expect some fumbling around trying to get everything done. It won't be a smooth transition.

Seldom Anticipated

Many pilots don't anticipate a missed approach unless the weather is at or below minimums. For example, your destination is reporting 500 overcast and 2 miles. The weather is above minimums, so you don't think about making a missed approach. What happens if you reach minimums and can't see the runway? You'll have to look at the approach chart to figure out what to do next. That will come after you deal with the surprise and anger you feel because the weather on the ATIS was wrong. Meanwhile the airplane sinks closer and closer to the ground.

The steps involved in making the missed approach vary from airplane to airplane, but upon realizing the runway isn't in sight, you must first get the nose to a climb attitude as you bring the throttles or power levers forward to takeoff power. Once takeoff power is established, you can get the gear and flaps up, but you must follow the missed approach procedure at the same time.

Brief Ahead

It's important to brief yourself on the missed approach procedure before beginning the approach. While you might not remember the holding pattern, you should be prepared to maneuver to a safe altitude and head toward the holding fix.

For example, say the missed approach procedure is a straight-ahead climb to 1500 feet before turning left to 320 degrees to the Blank Intersection. You must be at 2500 feet before reaching Blank, then hold North on the XYZ 010 radial. While the whole procedure is important, the critical part is climbing straight ahead to 1500 feet, then flying the 320 heading while climbing to 2500 feet before reaching Blank.

For a single pilot to memorize the entire missed approach procedure is sometimes difficult. You should at least remember the first part to get to a safe altitude (in this case 2500 feet), where you can look at the approach chart for the holding instructions.

We fly from a small airport with a VOR approach to each end of Runway 6/24. There have been several occasions where we've had to make a missed approach and proceed to our alternate, eight miles away. Upon declaring the missed approach to the tower they simply gave us a heading to fly and told us to contact approach control. When we got back to approach, the controller vectored us to the ILS at our alternate. Although we were prepared to fly the published missed approach, it wasn't necessary.

Early Miss

Sometimes you need to miss the approach before getting to the DH or MDA. We were inbound to New York JFK International when the entire east coast was low IFR in fog. JFK was at minimums for the ILS in use (200 and a half). The controller, having so much traffic backed up and wanting to get us out of the way quickly, vectored us to the localizer at the final approach fix without giving us enough time to intercept the glideslope.

When he cleared us for the approach, we were 1000 feet above the glideslope at the outer marker. We weren't about to dive the airplane from that position, so we declared a missed approach as we called the tower. The tower didn't understand and asked why we were going around. I quickly explained and the controller gave us a heading to fly and handed us back to approach control. We got back in the line up and flew it again.

Engine Failure

What if you lose an engine in a twin during a missed approach? It's your responsibility to ensure the airplane will perform. If you're in a mountainous area or at a facility that has particular climb requirements, check the missed approach procedure and be certain your airplane is capable of doing it.

What if you have a problem of some kind during the missed approach procedure? Your hands are already full just trying to get the airplane to a safe altitude. Remember, the first rule of instrument flying is, *Fly the airplane first.*

If the problem can wait until you're at a safe altitude, let it wait. If an engine fails, you must deal with it immediately. But don't forget to fly the airplane first.

If you're in high terrain or obstructions keep the airplane on course.

Get the engine secured and retrim the airplane so it will be easier to maintain directional control. *But above all, keep flying the airplane.*

Flying a missed approach procedure is the hardest part of instrument flying. If you have some kind of failure to deal with at the same time it will be that much harder. The key to successfully completing the maneuver is to be prepared to execute it in the first place. Look over the procedure and memorize the critical portion of it before starting the approach no matter what the weather.

It's all well and good to say that you should study the missed approach procedure ahead of time, but what about what happens in the real world?

In the real world we virtually never fly missed approaches, and frankly for most of us the skills get a bit rusty. It's all too easy to pay mere lip service to the missed approach procedure, and not be really prepared to fly it when a for-real missed approach does happen.

This section takes a look at some ways of pulling off a successful missed approach if you find yourself behind the eight ball when it comes time to throttle up and go.

The Unexpected Missed Approach

The thought of executing a missed approach in actual instrument conditions sends chills down the back of many instrument pilots. Part of the aversion to missed approaches comes from our instrument training, where we're told to memorize the entire missed approach procedure before starting the approach. We soon learn that there isn't always time to thoroughly digest the approach, much less to study the missed approach. We're told that the more time we spend studying and executing the approach itself, the less chance we'll have of missing the approach.

Preflight Preparation

If there's a time to study the missed approach procedure, it's during preflight. Although most instrument approaches have similar elements, all missed approaches are different. They require turns in different directions, climbs before and after the turns, and often the identification of navaids, radials and intersections that aren't related to the approach procedure. At the end of most missed approach procedures is a holding pattern. For most of us, holding pattern entries are far from our strong suit.

Our chances of a successful missed approach are better if we devote preflight time to studying the procedures. If, in order to complete the missed approach procedure, it's necessary to change the radio frequencies and re-set the VORs, we should rehearse these steps during preflight.

The Real World

Now let's talk about real-life. The most important missed approach you'll ever fly will come as a complete surprise. You won't be expecting it and you won't be prepared. Maybe the weather will suddenly go sour; maybe an accident will close the runway; maybe other circumstances will force you to divert to an unfamiliar airport and fly an unrehearsed approach.

Whatever the scenario, if you fly in the clouds long enough, the time will come when you'll arrive at the missed approach point of an unfamiliar airport while still in IMC. When this happens, the essence of good instrument flying is not how smoothly you can fly a well-rehearsed missed approach, but how successfully you execute the important steps of a procedure when caught with your pants down.

It's important for you to know, and truly believe, that you can fly any missed approach without prior preparation. The key to success is believing you can do it. On the other hand, the pilot who doubts, will panic and hesitate. When 200 feet above the approach lights, in the clouds and descending at 700 fpm, he who hesitates is certainly lost (apologies to William Shakespeare).

When teaching instrument ground school, we would tell our students that we had memorized the first two steps of every missed approach procedure in the country. Invariably a student would ask, "Okay, so what are the first two steps of the missed approach at Salina, Kansas?"

We would reply, "The first step is to climb and the second step is to turn." There are no missed approach procedures that require a descent from the missed approach point.

Although this might seem obvious, most pilots who crash on missed approaches do so because they failed to climb and/or failed to turn.

Two-Step Procedure

The first step in any missed approach procedure is a climb, either straight ahead or in a turn. If caught with a surprise missed approach, don't start reading the chart, start climbing. Everything that can hurt you is on the ground. You want to get as far away from the ground as quickly as possible. Bring the props and manifold pressure up to climb power, or up to full power, and concentrate on the attitude indicator.

Use the rudders to keep the wings level and you'll automatically correct for torque and P-factor.

When the climb attitude is established, retract the landing gear, retract the flaps if required and trim. Cross-check the pitch with the airspeed indicator, altimeter and VSI and make any necessary adjustments. Finally, check the setting of the throttles, propellers, mixture controls and cowl flaps. All these tasks must be performed regardless of the missed approach, so the fact that you don't know what comes next isn't important at this point.

Executing a missed approach also requires a report to ATC. Remember to follow the proper pilots priority: first aviate, then navigate, and finally, communicate. A call to ATC might result in the following: "Beech 12345, roger. Turn left heading 280, climb and maintain 3000." On the other hand, you could get into a prolonged exchange that could complicate the situation. If ATC makes things more difficult for you, tell them to stand by until you have more time.

Read Once Squared Away

If you keep the wings level, you shouldn't be too far off heading. Nevertheless, now is the time to check your heading, compare it to the course to be intercepted and turn to correct if necessary. Once you've trimmed for a maximum performance climb, and established a heading to intercept the missed approach course, it's time to read the instructions.

The instructions for the missed approach on the profile view of the chart can often be difficult to understand, especially when you're under stress. On the other hand, the graphic depiction of the missed approach on the plan view is easy to interpret immediately. If it shows a turn near the airport, the only question in your mind should be, "How high should I be before turning?" Read the first part of the missed approach instructions and you'll know.

Likewise, if the missed approach depiction shows a track straight from the airport before turning, ask yourself, "How do I determine when to turn?" The first part of the missed approach instructions will tell you. Look at the depiction first, then read the instructions.

Many of the complex turns and intermediate altitudes included in missed approach instructions are inserted to comply with overlapping authorities of air traffic control. If you are up to speed on the missed approach procedure, and if you can stop your climb until passing a fix that you haven't even identified yet, then good for you. But remember, the most important thing is taking care of the airplane and your passengers.

To the best of our knowledge, there has never been a mid-air collision in the clouds caused by a pilot overshooting an intermediate altitude on a missed approach procedure. On the other hand, the most common accident associated with missed approaches results from running into terrain or an obstacle. When in doubt, climb.

Entering The Hold

The next step in the missed approach usually involves entering a holding pattern at a specific altitude. When you reach holding pattern altitude, reduce power to low cruise and level off. Again, if you're mentally prepared, you can make a nice entry into the holding pattern. On the other hand, if your mind is still as foggy as the view out the window, go to the holding fix and turn by the shortest direction to the outbound heading for the holding pattern. After one minute outbound, head back to the fix. When you cross the fix, start holding.

Or you could find yourself at your assigned altitude with no idea where you are in the middle of a complicated missed approach procedure. In this case, you have no choice but to head directly for the holding fix. If the hold is at a VOR or an NDB, just fly to the station.

Intersection Holding

When the hold is at an intersection, you need a method to get you directly there. There's an easy way to do this: Dial up the two VORs that define the intersection, and set the intersection radials on the OBS. Determine the 90-degree intercept for each of the two radials, and split the differece. For example, say an intersection is formed by the 345° radial from one VOR, and the 255° radial from another. You set up your radios, and you see that the first CDI is to the left with a FROM flag, and the second is to the right with a FROM flag. This means you're somewhere between the two radials. with the intersection to the northwest of your present position. (Maintain positional awareness. It helps to be good at interpreting what your CDIs are telling you.)

The 90-degree intercept for the first VOR radial is 255°, and the second is 345°. Split the difference and you get 300°. Fly that heading until either CDI centers, then track the radial outbound until you reach the intersection.

Then the next time you take an instrument competency check or refresher training, have your flight instructor dial up VOR intersections so you can practice proceeding direct.

In the final analysis, if you get your airplane climbing smartly, if you follow the track onthe plan view of the missed approach procedure, if you don't turn the aircraft until you reach the first altitude in the missed approach instructions, and if you can get your airplane to the holding fix, you can fly any missed approach without preparation.

Keep Priorities Straight

We don't advocate flying missed approaches without preparation. But the day will come when you'll end up behind the eight ball and you can get out of a tough situation by climbing like a homesick angel, turning to the heading on the chart and entering the hold at the correct fix. You can fly any missed approach without preparation, if you keep your priorities in order and your wits about you.

Descent and Landing

We take it for granted that the established procedures we use when flying IFR are well reasoned and sensible. Generally that's true, but sometimes there are situations where the published procedure just doesn't make sense. One of these has to do with the final descent and landing from a non-precision approach.

Next time you look at a plate, ask yourself: Is it really possible to land if you catch sight of the airport at the MAP? Often it is, but not always.

Contributor and Air Force pilot J. Ross Russo here takes a common-sense look at establishing a reasonable descent to landing.

Window of Opportunity

Before I question everything you hold sacred about flying a missed approach, let me relate a brief story about the British Army during the early days of World War II. I think it holds an important lesson for instrument pilots.

Having just been driven out of Dunkirk, the Brits were working feverishly to fortify England's coastline against a German invasion. They were so desperate that some of the old artillery used during the Boer War was being pressed into service. In attempting to extract higher rates of fire from these antiques, commanders noticed a strange thing.

As the four-man team prepped the gun, there would be a blur of activity as they loaded the projectile and set the gun's elevation. Suddenly, all activity ceased as two of the crew moved to the rear, turned opposite the direction of fire and snapped sharply to attention. Two or three seconds later, the crew commander fired the cannon.

A researcher studying the problem asked the men about this. What was the reason for the turn and hesitation? The men had no explanation. They'd simply been trained to do it that way. Finally, in desperation, a film of the process was shown to a retired artillery colonel. When he asked to see the film in slow motion, the answer came to him:

"Of course," he exclaimed, "they're steadying the horses!"

Steadying the horses? There *weren't* any horses. Trucks had long since replaced the animals but the military, with its rigid adherence to tradition and training, had simply overlooked this little detail.

This story illustrates two interesting points about human nature. First, we're reluctant to question the way we've been trained. Pilots often take the word of their CFII as gospel, even though the instructor may be completely wrong. Second, most people are slaves to habit and averse to change, to the extent that we'll sometimes persist in an effort we know to be futile.

Case in point for this discussion is continuing an approach, straight and level at the minimum descent altitude when there's absolutely no hope of making a normal landing. From day one, we train to do this but it really makes very little sense.

Cockpit Movie

Let's imagine for a moment that we're sharing that artillery colonel's vantage but instead of a gun, we're watching a film of a pilot flying a non-precision approach in weather. We see the same flurry of activity as the pilot flies to the final approach fix, begins his descent to MDA and punches the clock. We watch the increased activity as the pilot levels at MDA and makes course corrections.

Then something strange happens. The airplane flies through the point where the MDA intersects the normal 3-degree glideslope to the runway. No activity. The pilot plods along at the same altitude. The airplane passes the point where the 6-degree slope intersects the MDA. From this point, there's no way the airplane can land on the runway using anything approaching the "normal descent" required by FAR 91.175. Yet, the pilot presses on, a slave to the watch and/or the approach plate.

Steadying the horses? It seems so. But that's the way most of us are trained. Fly on to the missed approach point, even if it's a mile or more past the point where a landing is even remotely possible.

The problem is pretty basic. Descending safely from the MDA—especially in poor visibility—needs to be done in an orderly fashion. A steep, high rate of descent, perhaps with a slip, is not the best way to go. We have to come up with a simple method to determine a descent from the MDA, a " window" from which we can descend to a normal landing without being too shallow or too steep.

The FAA has, to a certain extent, provided this on some approaches. It's called the visual descent point or VDP. It defines the point where the MDA meets the 3-degree glideslope. However, the VDP is of limited use because it's based on DME, which isn't available everywhere. And not long ago the FAA stopped using the VDP in new procedures.

What we really need is a way to determine a VDP from timing, so it can be used when DME isn't available. We have the technology to do this. Read on.

Second, in defining our window of opportunity, we need to know when a descent to landing will be too steep to meet the FAR's definition of "normal" or, more to the point, when it's too steep to be safe. That's always been the rub. What *is* the steepest "normal" glideslope?

I have my own theory. After reviewing endless heads-up display (HUD) tapes of new-guy landings in the F-16, I've concluded that for most airplanes, a descent path of 6 degrees is about as steep as can be considered normal. Most F-16 landings from a normal traffic pattern (an overhead approach from an initial point) are right around 5 or 6 degrees. The picture from the cockpit agrees with what I'd consider to be as steep as I'd care to be for a normal approach in anything from an F-16 to a Cessna 152. Also, as you'll see, using a 6-degree slope as the steep end of the window is convenient, considering it's twice the slope of what's considered the shallow end of the spectrum, the 3-degree slope.

For convenience, I'll call the 3-degree point the VDP and the 6-degree point the "pull-up point," or PUP. Interestingly, the MAP used to be called the PUP back in the early days of instrument flying. In between the VDP and PUP is our descent window, from which we descend to a normal landing.

Calculating PUP and VDP

Since we're most interested in the PUP, let's figure it first. Then, to find the VDP, we'll simply work backwards. Since the PUP slope is twice that of the VDP slope, the distance is merely doubled. In other words, if we compute the PUP to be 1 mile from the published MAP, the VDP will be at two miles. Simple.

I realize that there are basically three types of pilots: engineers who love complex charts and graphs; quasi-engineers who would love all those charts and graphs if they could just read them and guys (like me) who just want a good rule of thumb that'll work in the cockpit. The rule of thumb works best so that's what I'll concentrate on.

There are two ways to define the VDP and PUP. The easiest is to use DME or, as an aid to your IFR-approved navigation equipment, a loran or GPS. The second method is to use timing. Let's consider DME first and how to use it as a descent aid. What we have to do is convert our desired glideslope angle to a descent gradient. (Don't worry, it's not necessary to haul out the gradient-rate tables: This is a rule of thumb, and like all good rules of thumb it's both easy to remember and easy to work.)

Here's an easy way: The descent angle is equal to the number of feet in hundreds per nautical mile. In other words, a 3-degree slope requires a descent of 300 feet per nautical mile; a 6-degree slope requires 600 feet per mile. To turn it around, to descend 100 feet on a 6-degree slope requires 1/6 mile. For the 3-degree slope, going down 100 feet takes 1/3 mile.

So defining the PUP and VDP is easy. Just look at the height above touchdown (HAT) and figure how far the PUP will have to be backed up from the approach end of the runway by using a factor of 1/6 nautical mile for each 100 feet of HAT.

Let's take a dirt-simple example, with a HAT on the low side: 325 feet. The PUP will be 3/6 of a mile (0.5) from the end of the runway. this is another way of saying that if you see the runway at 0.4 mile, you can't land on it using a normal descent.

VDPs

How about the VDP? Just as easy. It's twice the PUP's distance from the runway or 1/3 mile per hundred feet above the touchdown.

Here's another example, a little more complex: You're shooting a VOR DME approach with a HAT of 600 feet. The VOR is located on the field, exactly halfway down a 6000-foot runway.

In a classic approach, the published MAP would be at approximately 0.5 DME, directly over the approach end of the runway or perhaps even over the VOR itself. But using the formula for the PUP, the latest point from which we can make a normal descent to the approach end of the runway is one mile *prior* to the MAP or at 1.5 DME from the navaid. (The PUP or 6-degree slope is equal to 1/6 mile for each 100 feet of HAT. We have 600 feet to descend, so that's 6/6, or one mile. The extra half-mile is because the VOR is halfway down a mile-long runway, and is reflected by the 0.5 DME location of the MAP. If you prefer decimals, use 0.16 instead of 1/6 mile.)

To find the VDP, we simply double the 1 mile used for the PUP. That yields a VDP at 2 miles prior to the published MAP, or 2.5 miles from the vortac.

So, as we slog along at the MDA, we know that a descent prior to 2.5 miles will cause us to be shallow and trying for the runway any closer than 1.5 DME will put us steeper than what might be considered healthy. So, the normal landing window is between 2.5 DME (VDP) and 1.5 DME (PUP) on final. Continue at the MDA past the PUP and you're wasting your time steadying the horses. There's just no way you're gong to get onto the runway safely.

What if the runway is 10,000 feet long? Okay, different situation. In that case, it may be perfectly acceptable to start the descent at the PUP or a little beyond and still land with runway to spare. You'd want to work that out ahead of time, of course. This applies only to Part 91 pilots. For-hire pilots have to land in the touchdown zone, which is the first 3000 feet of the runway. And, in any case, 10,000-foot runways are likely to be air carrier airports and will be served by an ILS in any case.

So, to summarize:

- Find the HAT in the minimums box on the approach plate. Round it to the nearest hundred feet.
- For every hundred feet, move the PUP 1/6 mile back from the MAP.
- Double the PUP distance for the VDP.

Timing the PUP

So much for the easy stuff. Now let's look at determining the normal landing window by timing. Take a look at the angle and descent tables Jeppesen and NOS provide. You'll notice that there are groundspeeds along the top of the table and angle of descent or glideslope angle along the left. On the Jeppesen charts, there are also times from a fix (usually the non-precision FAF) to the MAP. Jeppesen prints this data right on the bottom of ILS plates; NOS puts it on the inside back cover of the booklet.

What these tables do is provide a required descent rate at a given groundspeed to achieve a certain glideslope angle. Using the Jepp table for our previous example shows that at a typical 90-knot groundspeed, we would need a 487 fpm descent to achieve a 3-degree slope. Double that (974 fpm) to calculate the 6-degree slope.

This really shows the validity of using 6 degrees as the maximum slope. At 90 knots in my Twin Comanche, 974 fpm on short final is as high a descent rate as I'd ever care to see. I'd much prefer the more gentle and stable 487 fpm.

Now, since we know the vertical velocity necessary to maintain the glideslope as well as the altitude to lose from the HAT, it's easy to determine the time required. Using an E-6B, place the number of feet to be lost (HAT) above the required vertical velocity for your desired airspeed and read the number of seconds above the index (actually, the number 60) on the inner scale. Simple stuff on the ground, right? But in the airplane, it'd by like trying to stack greased BBs. A better way is to calculate a series of pre-figured tables that correct or amend the published timing to allow for a homemade VDP and PUP.

As a long-time subscriber to the theory that it does no good to measure with a micrometer if you intend to mark with a crayon and cut with an axe, I realize that you'll need a simple way to do this or you'll never bother with it. So, I've boiled it down to three numbers. You use the one that corresponds to your approach groundspeed. Each number is multiplied by the HAT in hundreds, and the result is subtracted from the MAP timing.

For 70-90 knots, subtract 7 seconds for each 100 feet of HAT; for 90-100 knots, 6 seconds, and 100 to 120 knots, 5 seconds.

This gives you the PUP. Again, for VDP just double what you get for PUP.

For example, for a HAT of 400 feet and a ground speed of 90 knots, you'd knock 28 seconds (round up to 30) off the published time for the PUP. Double that and knock a full minute off for the VDP. That means one minute before the published time is up, you should be looking for the runway and preparing for the descent. Thirty seconds before the published time has elapsed, don't bother. You're steadying the horses.

To summarize:

• Find the HAT in the minimums box on the approach plate. Round it to the nearest hundred feet.

• For every hundred feet, figure the appropriate time correction as follows:

70-90 kt	7 sec.
90-100 kt	6 sec
100-110 kt	5 sec

Subtract the time you get from the published MAP timing to get PUP. Round it for convenience.

• Double the PUP time correction for the VDP.

Descent Rates

How about the requisite descent rate? That's easy, too. Multiply groundspeed by 10 for the PUP; you'll need 900 fpm at 90 knots. For the VDP, take half of that value and you'll have a reasonable figure for descent rate from the VDP. This is a clean and simple method, requiring nothing more than simple math and minimal cockpit clutter.

If you have DME aboard, you can use the DME factor, too. As previously mentioned, it's 1/6 mile (.16) per 100 feet of HAT. The .16 is easy to remember: sweet 16, F-16, 16 is the age to require to solo, whatever.

Using it All

How does this all come together in the air? Here's what I recommend. Instead of using just timing or DME to determine a MAP, use everything available: DME, loran, GPS or timing to determine a normal landing window. That window is between the VDP (3-degree slope) and PUP (6-degree slope).

Use whatever rate of descent is required to arrive at the MDA prior to the VDP. Unless you're willing to request and receive a contact approach, don't even consider descending below the MDA until you reach your VDP, especially at night or on an unfamiliar approach. Also, unless you're flying a STOL aircraft or approaching a very long runway, you're just whistling in the wind if you continue flight at the MDA past the PUP.

Therefore, get close to three sets of numbers on a non-precision approach (not counting altitudes). Start looking for the runway at the VDP, continue until the PUP, and then, if you can't meet the visual requirements to land, start a straight-ahead climb until you reach the published MAP. From there, execute the published missed approach. Since you know that anything beyond the PUP will put you too steep for a normal approach, why stay at the MDA? I don't recommend starting any turns prior to the MAP but the extra altitude you'll have by starting the climb 30 seconds to a minute sooner is certainly a bonus. Nothing in the regs says you can't start the missed approach sooner than recommended.

There's another situation where being able to determine a VDP and PUP will prove valuable, even when operating VFR at a field with no approach. It's when you're landing at night on a runway that's not served by any glide slope information (VASI, PAPI, ILS). It's probably safest to delay your descent until reaching the PIP, whether you're VFR or completing an instrument approach. that 6-degree glideslope could provide a buffer between you and any unseen obstacles that may be in your path.

I remember one night landing at College Park, Maryland. I'd never been there but the approach looked fine, except for some shadows of some sort just noticeable as the wingtip strobes fired.

the landing was uneventful and I didn't give the shadows a second thought, until the next day when I was pre-flighting for the trip home. When I examined the approach path in the light of day, I saw that the shadows were caused by a big, tree-covered hill on final. There were no lights on the hill or structures of any kind so it was invisible at night.

Had I used the PUP technique, I could have stayed comfortably above the hill and still been in a position to execute a normal landing. Too bad I didn't know about the technique back then.

So, are you ready to give the PUP method a try or are you chained to a single all-or-nothing point in space? Try the method in your airplane (preferably in good weather, on an approach you know, and with a safety pilot) and see if these numbers aren't accurate.

You may need that extra half-minute of climb only once during your entire career as an instrument pilot. Or a bit of help on a night landing might keep you out of the trees or wires just once in a lifetime.

So far we've looked extensively at getting down the final approach course to a position from which we can either land or call it quits and execute the missed approach. What about that crucial transition from flying the approach to getting set up for a landing?

It's a mistake to think that the approach is over when you reach the MAP. The approach doesn't end until you're safely on the ground or holding at the missed approach holding fix. So much attention is paid to being where you need to be on the approach itself that it's all too easy to ignore the planning necessary to actually get on the ground once you break out of the clouds. This chapter looks at what to be aware of during the last part of a successful approach.

The Last Few Seconds

An instrument approach is designed to get you low enough to see either the landing runway or one of the visual references specified by FAR 91.175. For many approaches, especially those of the non-precision variety, the missed approach point is at the runway threshold or beyond. If a runway is long enough, and you break out just before or at the missed approach point, there might be enough room to get down safely, but often that's not the case. As we saw in the last section on VDPs, to make a reasonable descent you need to be able to see the runway well before you reach the MAP.

On short runways, spotting the runway or airport environment at the last minute can lead to a bad landing or worse. In this situation, you might be tempted to dive at the runway while allowing airspeed to increase. A descent from 400 feet agl or higher close to or over the approach end of the runway could require a longer stretch of pavement than the amount available. Many pilots don't realize that transitioning from an approach to a landing requires time and distance. Let's look at both and the effects on an instrument arrival.

How to Configure

A properly flown ILS puts you in the best position for a landing by descending you to within 200 feet of the runway. How do you fly an ILS in your airplane? The configuration and speeds depend on the aircraft and sometimes there will be differences between various models of the same machine. So let's generalize here to get the point across that even an ILS requires preparation for landing after spotting the runway. Our model approach will be flown by a high-performance single. You might not do things exactly the way we've outlined them here, but the result should still be the same.

Refer to the ILS Runway 27 at Flint, Michigan (pp 166-167). Suppose the controller vectors you to the localizer between Harro and Dortt and clears you down to 2000 feet. The normal approach airspeed for your aircraft is 100 knots and the speed over the fence is 85 knots. However, your descent gets delayed, but the target altitude of 2000 feet seems attainable in time to reduce speed for the approach.

You intercept the localizer four miles from Dortt at 120 knots. When the DME indicates 5.9 (two miles from Dortt) you lower approach flaps. As the glideslope needle drops to one dot above center, you lower the gear. You reduce power to 17 inches and slide down the glideslope at 100 knots indicated, just where you should be.

It's a foggy day with a 200-foot ceiling and one-half mile visibility. At 1200 feet (almost 200 feet above DH) you peek, but are still IMC. You look again at minimums and spot the approach lights and runway.

Let's pause for a moment and consider a couple of options. First, this runway is 7200 feet; plenty of room to roll out on. You could leave the flaps at the approach setting and slowly reduce power while raising the nose in order to reduce speed during the last half mile. Depending on how skillful you are at reducing speed while descending, you'll probably touch down at or just beyond the touchdown zone on the runway.

On the other hand, if you lower full flaps at DH, the nose will pitch up and the airspeed will decrease. Anticipate the pitch change and lower the nose to maintain the glideslope or VASI, then let the speed bleed down to the normal landing speed. Some additional power might be required with full flaps. You might touch down short of the normal touchdown zone, but it also will be an acceptable landing.

Now let's shorten the runway to 3000 feet. Breaking out at DH, you

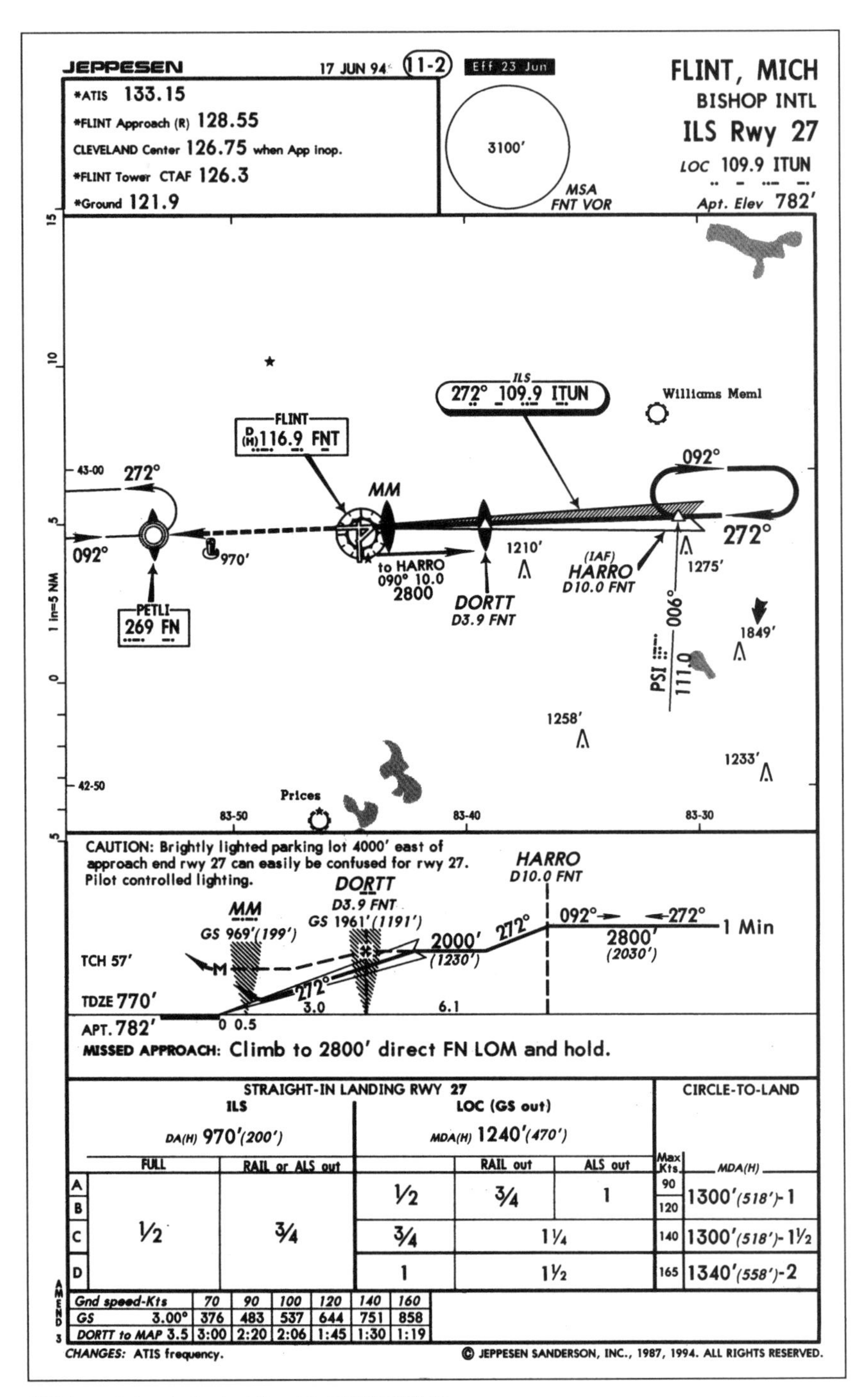
JEPPESEN
17 JUN 94
11-2
Eff 23 Jun
FLINT, MICH
BISHOP INTL
ILS Rwy 27
LOC 109.9 ITUN
Apt. Elev 782'
*ATIS 133.15
*FLINT Approach (R) 128.55
CLEVELAND Center 126.75 when App inop.
*FLINT Tower CTAF 126.3
*Ground 121.9
3100'
MSA
FNT VOR
ILS
272° 109.9 ITUN
Williams Meml
FLINT
116.9 FNT
43-00
272°
092°
MM
970'
to HARRO
090° 10.0
2800
1210'
(IAF)
HARRO
D10.0 FNT
1275'
272°
092°
DORTT
D3.9 FNT
PETLI
269 FN
006°
PSI
111.0
1849'
1258'
1233'
42-50
Prices
83-50
83-40
83-30
1 in=5 NM
CAUTION: Brightly lighted parking lot 4000' east of approach end rwy 27 can easily be confused for rwy 27.
Pilot controlled lighting.
HARRO
D10.0 FNT
DORTT
D3.9 FNT
GS 1961'(1191')
MM
GS 969'(199')
2000'
(1230')
272°
092°
272°
1 Min
2800'
(2030')
TCH 57'
TDZE 770'
APT. 782'
0 0.5
3.0
6.1
MISSED APPROACH: Climb to 2800' direct FN LOM and hold.
STRAIGHT-IN LANDING RWY 27
ILS
DA(H) 970'(200')
LOC (GS out)
MDA(H) 1240'(470')
CIRCLE-TO-LAND
FULL
RAIL or ALS out
RAIL out
ALS out
Max Kts
MDA(H)
A
B
C
D
½
¾
½
¾
1
¾
1¼
1
1½
90
120
1300'(518')-1
140
1300'(518')-1½
165
1340'(558')-2
Gnd speed-Kts 70 90 100 120 140 160
GS 3.00° 376 483 537 644 751 858
DORTT to MAP 3.5 3:00 2:20 2:06 1:45 1:30 1:19
AMEND 3
CHANGES: ATIS frequency.
© JEPPESEN SANDERSON, INC., 1987, 1994. ALL RIGHTS RESERVED.

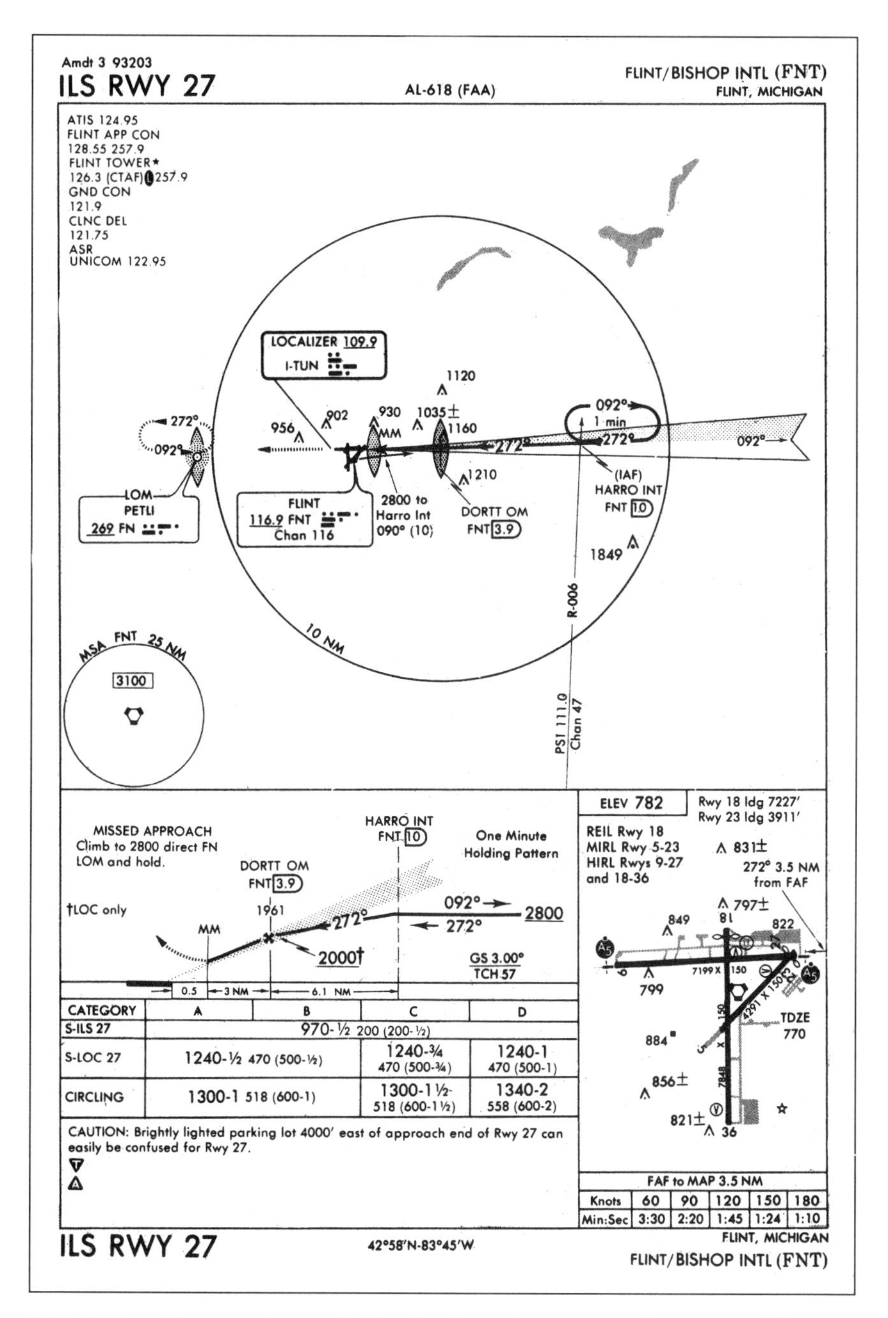

This ILS guides you to one-half mile from the runway, but you still must transition for a landing. Your speed during the approach along with aircraft configuration will determine where you'll touch down.

see the runway and know you must get it down and stopped. You don't have the luxury of rolling out on the runway for as long as it takes. The airspeed must be under control and the touchdown within reasonable parameters on the runway. If you allow the aircraft to float before touchdown due to excessive airspeed, you could easily run into trouble at the end, especially if the runway is wet or icy. How would you go about it?

Either method described above is acceptable provided you can maintain the proper airspeed. A 3000-foot runway for a high- performance single should be sufficient, but once some pilots spot the runway, they pitch down and ignore the airspeed.

Also, the visibility under the clouds, especially at night, could create an illusion that distorts your depth perception and peripheral vision. In this situation, you could flare and suddenly realize you're too fast. This often leads to either planting the airplane on the runway and standing on the brakes or attempting a go around (which would be difficult if you aren't prepared).

The last half-mile on an ILS is where you transition from the approach to a landing. The airplane must be configured for the touchdown and the proper airspeed to avoid floating far down the pavement.

Non-Precision Traps

A non-precision approach leaves even less of a margin, especially if the missed approach point is at the runway threshold or beyond. This is one reason the visibility requirements are higher, so you'll see the runway in time to make a normal approach and landing. If you have a method of determining distance from the missed approach point, e.g., DME, loran or GPS, select a point beyond which a safe landing is no longer possible. You can use the PUP method outlined in the last section to good advantage here.

As noted previously, some non-precision approaches have a visual descent point (VDP); the point at which you should descend for (normally) a three-degree descent angle from the MDA to the runway. If you don't have the runway in sight at the VDP and continue the approach, be prepared for a higher than normal descent before reaching the missed approach point.

There are many approaches that don't have a VDP for guidance. The VOR Runway 9 at Manistee, Michigan (pp 170-171) is a good example. The missed approach point is just beyond the end of the runway. There are DME and non-DME minimums.

In this example, Runway 9 is 5500 feet, but there's a potential trap waiting if you don't keep track of the distance from the runway. Would you be able to land safely if you broke out over the approach end at 500 feet agl?

To avoid this situation, you could calculate your own visual descent point at 2.5 DME, which is 1.3 nm from the runway threshold. This VDP will be close to where you'll reach the straight-in MDA of 1100 feet and (if you have the runway in sight) will give you close to three-degree descent angle to the runway. The potential trap is that the VOR is the missed approach point and at the end of the runway. So, if you continue tracking to the VOR, still planning to make a landing if you break out, you might wind up bending the airplane and yourself.

Think about it for a minute. If you break out over the end of the runway you have just about one mile to recognize it, transition from the approach to a landing, get the airplane down on the runway (from 500 feet agl) and stopped. Can this be done in one mile?

In a high performance single or twin your approach speed will be 100 knots or more. When you see the runway you drop the flaps and reduce power, but what will happen to the airspeed when you lower the nose and dive at the runway? That will depend on whether your attention is strictly on the runway itself or whether you are paying attention to the instruments as well. But the chances of getting down and stopped safely from that position are slim to none.

Should you make a missed approach at your VDP if you don't see the runway? No. Just be aware that from that point on the more impractical a landing becomes because you may be too high to get down safely. And if your airspeed is on the high side when you do spot the runway it will be that much more difficult. With 5500 feet it appears you have more leeway than on a shorter runway, but don't be fooled. While you have more pavement, you still must see the runway or environment, transition from the approach to a landing and get the airplane safely down on the runway and stopped. It's just as easy to run off the end of a 5500-foot runway than a 3500-foot runway if you don't have airspeed under control, don't have enough time to make the transition properly or if the runway is directly under you and you dive at it from 500 feet.

As mentioned in the last section, the only way to devise a VDP for this approach if you don't have DME or another approved method of measuring distance to the missed approach point is through a timing rule of thumb. If you don't calculate one, you'll be looking for the runway while waiting to cross the VOR. The minimums are higher without DME, so you'll be 600 feet above the airport. Again, be cautious about spotting the runway and diving at it. If you don't have enough time to transition for a landing or if your speed is too high or you can't make a normal descent to the runway, don't attempt it.

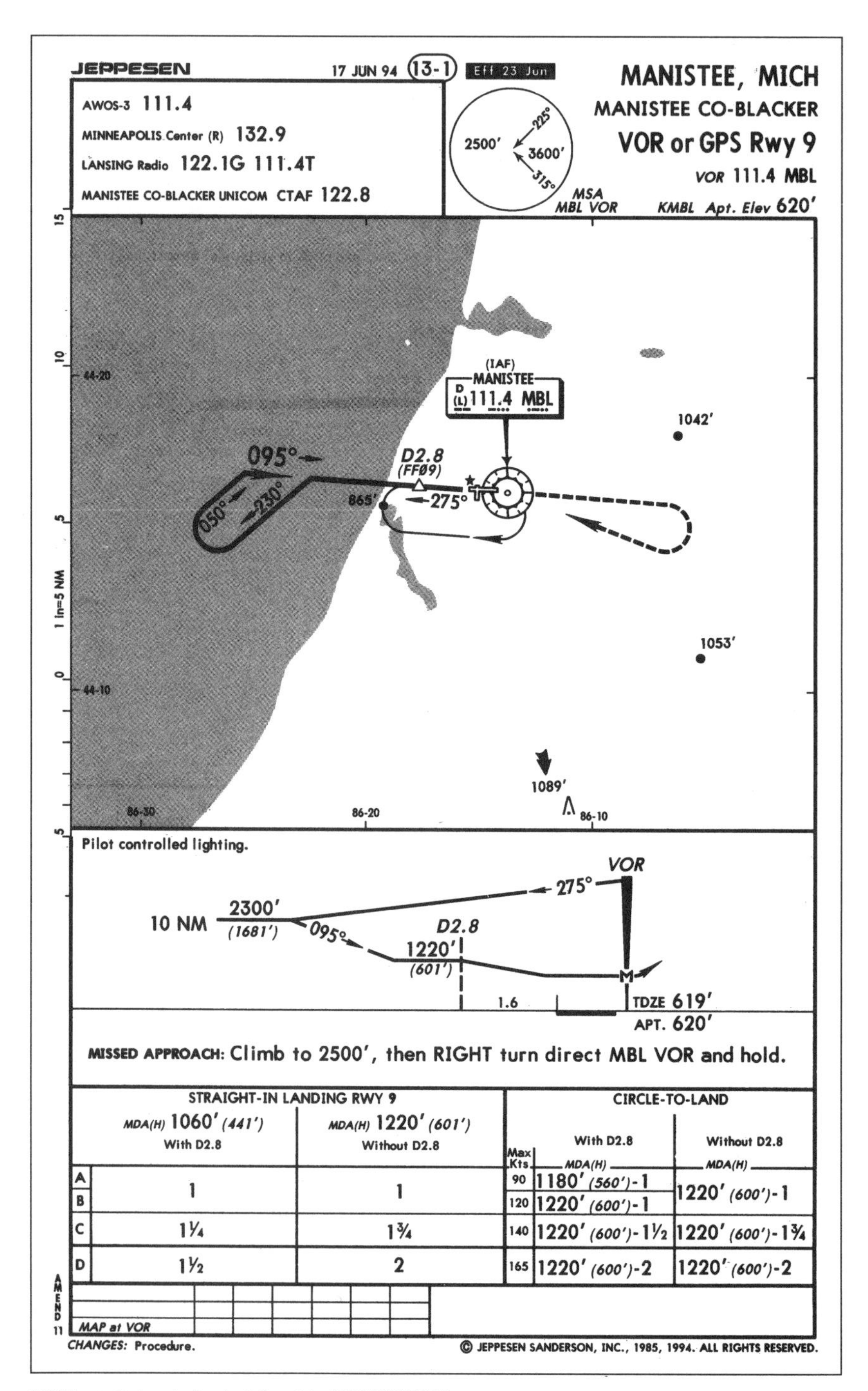

JEPPESEN
17 JUN 94
13-1
Eff 23 Jun
MANISTEE, MICH
MANISTEE CO-BLACKER
VOR or GPS Rwy 9
VOR 111.4 MBL
KMBL Apt. Elev 620'
AWOS-3 111.4
MINNEAPOLIS Center (R) 132.9
LANSING Radio 122.1G 111.4T
MANISTEE CO-BLACKER UNICOM CTAF 122.8
2500'
225°
3600'
315°
MSA
MBL VOR
(IAF)
MANISTEE
111.4 MBL
1042'
095°
D2.8
(FF09)
865'
275°
050°
230°
1053'
44-20
44-10
86-30
86-20
86-10
1089'
1 In=5 NM
Pilot controlled lighting.
VOR
275°
10 NM
2300'
(1681')
095°
D2.8
1220'
(601')
1.6
TDZE 619'
APT. 620'
MISSED APPROACH: Climb to 2500', then RIGHT turn direct MBL VOR and hold.
STRAIGHT-IN LANDING RWY 9
MDA(H) 1060' (441') With D2.8
MDA(H) 1220' (601') Without D2.8
CIRCLE-TO-LAND
Max Kts
With D2.8 MDA(H)
Without D2.8 MDA(H)
A
B
C
D
1
1
1¼
1¾
1½
2
90 1180' (560')-1
120 1220' (600')-1
1220' (600')-1
140 1220' (600')-1½
1220' (600')-1¾
165 1220' (600')-2
1220' (600')-2
AMEND 11
MAP at VOR
CHANGES: Procedure.
© JEPPESEN SANDERSON, INC., 1985, 1994. ALL RIGHTS RESERVED.

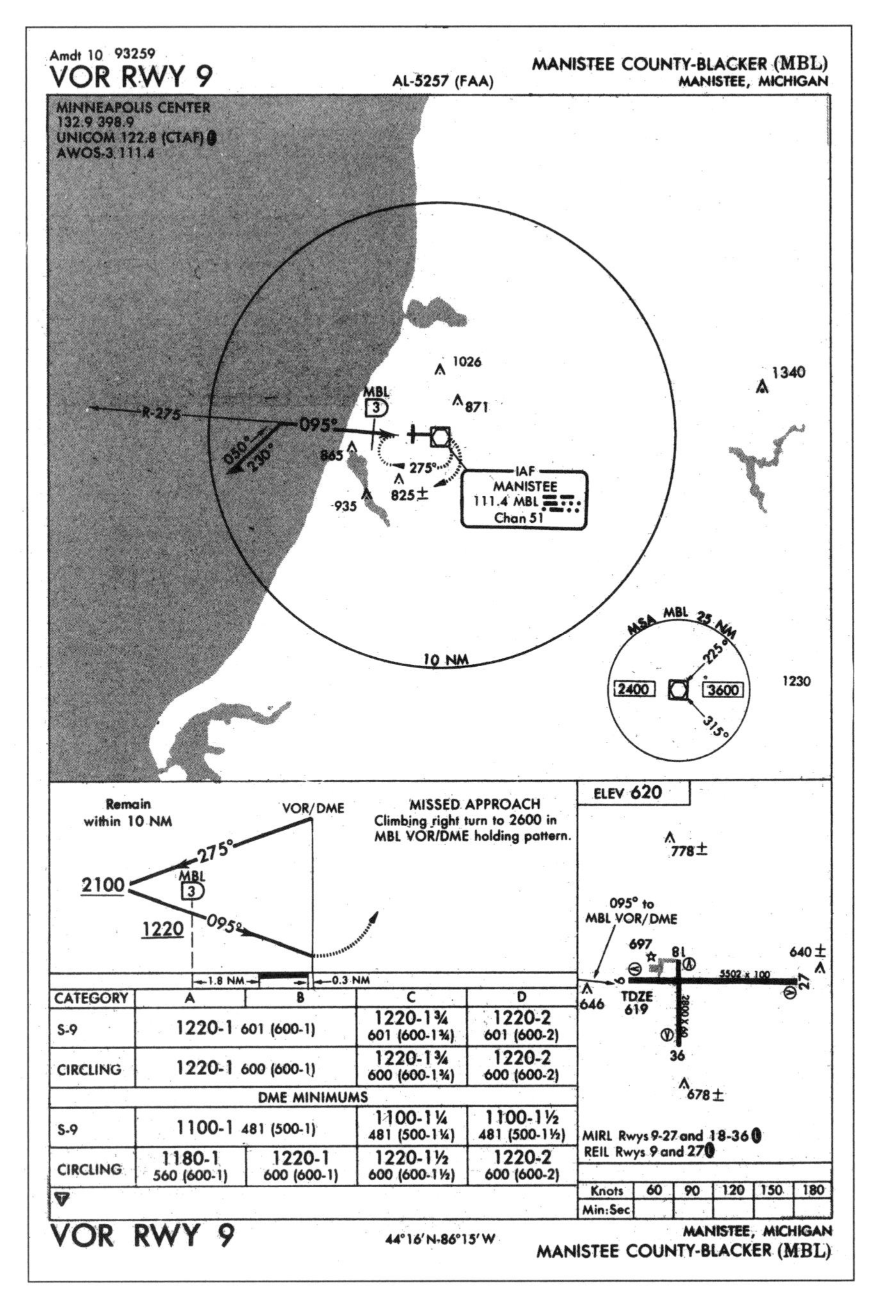

CATEGORY	A	B	C	D
S-9	1220-1 601 (600-1)		1220-1¾ 601 (600-1¾)	1220-2 601 (600-2)
CIRCLING	1220-1 600 (600-1)		1220-1¾ 600 (600-1¾)	1220-2 600 (600-2)
DME MINIMUMS				
S-9	1100-1 481 (500-1)		1100-1¼ 481 (500-1¼)	1100-1½ 481 (500-1½)
CIRCLING	1180-1 560 (600-1)	1220-1 600 (600-1)	1220-1½ 600 (600-1½)	1220-2 600 (600-2)

Knots	60	90	120	150	180
Min:Sec					

The trap waiting here is that the MAP is the far end of the runway. You'll be tempted to think of your DME reading as distance to the runway threshold. Calculating a VDP/PUP is useful in situations like this.

Circling Approaches

Another temptation for some pilots is the circling maneuver. There is nothing wrong with a circling approach provided you've planned for it. While most circling approaches require at least one mile visibility, don't attempt to circle unless you're certain you can keep the runway in sight throughout the maneuver.

Problems usually occur when a pilot flies a straight-in approach and sees the runway while passing overhead, then decides to circle back to that runway or to another one. Since circling minimums are usually higher than straight-in minimums, you must make either a straight-in approach or go around once you've descended below circling minimums.

Let's look at two other situations: an unlimited ceiling and poor visibility and a low ceiling with good visibility. While you still must see the runway in time to make a safe landing the scenario could change.

For example, with an unlimited ceiling and low visibility (as in summer haze), you can see the ground during the approach. If you're familiar with the area you'll know exactly where you are and that makes your job much easier. While you still cannot descend below the MDA until you have the airport or runway environment in sight, the transition from the approach to the landing will be easier. Depending on the forward visibility, you'll know when you should see the runway and will be prepared for the transition.

In the second scenario, where the visibility under the ceiling is good, how you conduct the approach can make the difference between seeing the runway in time to make a reasonable descent to a landing or not. Using the methods described earlier in the book, we like to descend to the MDA as early as possible on a non-precision approach. To accomplish this, we don't just push the nose down in a screaming dive as I pass the final approach fix.

Instead, we manage the distance to a given point and try to be at the appropriate minimum altitude before reaching the fix. For example, on the Manistee VOR 9 approach, once we're established on final and am within 10 nm of the VOR we can descend to 1220 feet. If we don't have DME we want to get down as early as possible, level off and search for the airport. Of course, if we maintain MDA and don't break out before reaching the VOR, we will be going around. But if we break out and see the runway we'll have more time to complete the transition from approach to landing.

With DME, we plan on being at 1220 feet by 4 DME at the latest, cross the 3 DME fix at that altitude, then immediately descend to 1100 feet while keeping track of my distance to the runway. We would prefer to be at the lower MDA between 1.5 and 1.25 miles from the runway if we don't see the airport before the 3 DME fix. Again, that provides sufficient time to locate the runway, transition from approach to landing and conduct a reasonable descent to the runway.

Fortunately, the ceiling and/or visibility are usually high enough that a descent to MDA or DH is not necessary before seeing the airport. Also, your personal minimums may not allow you to conduct an instrument approach to absolute minimums. If that is the case then simply intercepting the VASI, if there is one, or beginning a visual descent at a reasonable distance from the runway while keeping your airspeed within the parameters you select will ensure a safe touchdown early enough on the runway to stop safely.

If it's been a while since you've done an approach to minimums, practice a few with an instructor or safety pilot. Be sure you understand just how much room you need in your airplane to transition to the landing mode. Try, under controlled conditions, pulling the hood off at the missed approach point and seeing how quickly you can spot the runway, reconfigure the aircraft and attempt to get down. If you've never done this it's an exercise that will make you think when you get to the MDA or spot the runway close in during the real thing.

What happens if the only approach available to you is downwind, and the conditions are too low for a circle? Can you land safely?

The answer is a qualified "yes." Downwind landings aren't really taught, but they're certainly possible, provided there's a lot of runway and little wind. Sometimes it's the only way to make it into the airport.

Downwind Approach and Landing

You're just outside the outer marker on the ILS to Runway 25, when the tower tells you that the winds are from 70 degrees at 10 knots. The ceiling is 400 overcast and the visibility is one mile in rain. In typical monotone, the controller says, "Say your intentions."

A circling approach under a 400-foot ceiling is out of the question. Assuming there isn't an ILS to Runway 07, you can either execute a missed approach and go somewhere else, or land downwind.

Fast Touchdown

In a normal landing, the headwind reduces the actual touchdown speed. If you touch down at 60 knots, a 15-knot headwind results in a touchdown groundspeed of only 45 knots. Landing downwind in this situation, the touchdown groundspeed is 75 knots, a considerable difference.

If, for example, you normally flare five seconds prior to touchdown when landing into the wind, it will still take five seconds to dissipate speed when landing downwind. It isn't the time that changes, but the distance traveled in that period of time that causes problems.

When landing downwind, the flare seems to take forever and you're tempted to rush the landing. Don't let the airplane settle onto the runway before it's ready or add forward pressure on the controls to force it on. Either action results in bouncing off the nose wheel or wheelbarrowing down the runway.

Downwind landings should be performed exactly the same as normal landings. Let the airplane settle into ground effect and hold it off until it drops onto the runway at or near a stall. The problems come from the amount of real estate covered in the process, the speed at which things go by and the amount of runway remaining after touchdown.

Practice Difficult

Although most of us would benefit from practicing downwind landings, it's exceedingly difficult to find a place to practice them. If there's any traffic in the pattern, those pilots will want to land into the wind. At an uncontrolled field, regardless of how often you announce your position, it's always possible to encounter a no-radio airplane head-on.

At controlled airports, the tower may be reluctant to allow downwind landings due to a potential conflict with other traffic approaching or entering the pattern.

A downwind landing can usually be practiced at the end of an ILS in VFR conditions, since the controller has already reconciled to the disruption to traffic due to the approach. When circling instructions are given, ask if you can take a shot at a downwind landing.

Downwind ILS

A downwind ILS provides another insidious factor in the downwind landing. Invariably, you arrive over the touchdown zone with excess airspeed since the tailwind on the approach causes you to over-fly the glideslope.

The normal reaction is to add forward pressure on the controls and increase the rate of descent which, of course, increases the airspeed. So most often, a pilot making a downwind landing from a downwind approach crosses the threshold with both excess airspeed and a horrendous groundspeed.

How Much Does it Add?

On all flight reviews and instrument competency checks, we ask about the effect of a 10-knot tailwind on landing distance. Most pilots guess that the distance increases 10-25 percent. Real pessimists run the figure up to 50 percent.

Yet the correct answer is twice that. When all factors are added in, including high airspeed from the downwind approach, higher yet groundspeed from the tailwind and lack of pilot proficiency in the maneuver, an airplane will usually take twice the distance to land that it normally would. If 2000 feet would be tight for your airplane, don't even attempt a downwind landing from a downwind approach with less than 4000 of runway.

When you break-out, identify a spot halfway down the runway as a go-around point. If the airplane is still flying when you get there, add full power and go around.

Fortunately, most runways at the end of ILS approaches are quite long. If you hold the airplane off and use aerodynamic breaking to slow to near stall before touchdown, a safe downwind landing can usually be made. You should set your own limits in this situation. Ours is ten knots. If the tailwind exceeds this, we don't even consider a downwind landing.

Crosswinds

Although most runways with an ILS are plenty long, they can appear narrow when there's a crosswind, or worse yet, a quartering tailwind. Like the downwind landing, most of us shy away from the crosswind landing and use the runway that points into the wind. The problems of aircraft control are also compounded by a wet runway that often accompanies a low ceiling.

Considerable debate rages over the best technique to use in a crosswind landing. Advocates of the slip method are adamant about the merits of their technique. Those who have mastered the crab-kick-cuss method are equally enamored with their procedure.

Regardless of the technique used, the time will arrive when you're no longer flying but steering a fast moving airplane down a very slick runway. If the wheels hydroplane, either because of too much speed, a puddle on the runway, or a sudden application of the brakes, the pilot who holds full aileron into the crosswind will track straight.

On the other hand, the airplane with neutral ailerons will drift downwind. In order to correct, the pilot of the drifting airplane must either put the controls into a slip configuration, or add sufficient rudder to allow the airplane to crab while sliding down the runway. Either way, the pilot who is caught flat footed, with the ailerons in neutral when the airplane suddenly drifts downwind, will be on a wild ride.

The best crosswind landing technique seems to be one where the airplane is slipped into the wind. After touchdown, the amount of aileron deflection into the wind is increased to the stop. In this configuration, the airplane has the best chance of staying on the runway.

Also, you don't get any points for landing on the runway center line. On a wet and treacherous runway, it's better to touch down on the upwind edge of the runway and slide into the middle than it is to touchdown in the middle and slide into the lights.

Excess speed is a big factor in hydroplaning, which is the point where the aircraft tires slide on top of the water instead of rolling on the runway. The hydroplaning speed of your airplane is equal to nine times the square root of the tire pressure. For example, your main wheels have a pressure of 50 psi. The square root of 50 is approximately 7. Multiply 7 times 9 and the hydroplaning speed is 63 knots. If you touch down faster than 63 knots on a wet runway, the airplane will probably hydroplane. Therefore, when landing downwind the chances of hydroplaning are much greater than when landing into the wind.

In this situation, it's especially important to slow the airplane as much as possible prior to touchdown. At a time when all your instincts are screaming to get on the ground, you must resist the temptation to let the airplane land hot. It's better to hold the airplane off the runway a little higher than you normally would, and allow it to flop onto the runway, than to risk touching down fast. Also remember, new tires with deep grooves and proper inflation are less likely to hydroplane than worn-out tires.

Helpful Techniques

The downwind or crosswind landing to a wet runway is one of those times where you must perform flawlessly with little or no practice, there are several exercises which can help a great deal.

First, if you've gotten into the habit of landing your tricycle- gear airplane hot, or if occasionally the nose wheel touches down first or the airplane lands in a three-point attitude, it's time to break the habit. Practice full stall landings with the wind down the runway and with a crosswind until you are comfortable holding the airplane off. If you can't do it in the calm of a practice session, you certainly won't be able to do it under stress.

Another exercise is to fly the approach 10-20 knots faster than usual. This looks and feels like a downwind landing. It requires you to exercise patience while the runway speeds by. Of course, keep an eye on your progress and if an overshoot looks possible, add power and go around.

VFR crosswind landing practice is also good preparation. If you can't plant the airplane where you want it and make it stay there, you better stay off wet runways until you can.

When the weather nears minimums and a circling approach is risky, it can be impossible to complete the maneuver safely and legally. Under these circumstances, you're compelled to make a straight-in approach to the runway aligned with the final approach course. If you're proficient at downwind and crosswind landings, you can often safely use an airport that others should avoid.

• Section Four •

Approach Fine Points

Procedure Turns

In the current ATC radar environment, procedure turns are often not used, especially if you fly in one of the more congested parts of the country. If the controller can vector you (and thereby get you the heck out of the way), he or she will do so.

The busier the airport, the less likely you'll ever see a procedure turn. Major terminals don't even have them.

Still, they're on nearly all approach plates, just in case. And you have to know how to deal with them. The good news is that they're easy. You have a lot of room to play with, and you can accomplish the maneuver pretty much any way you want to.

To Turn or Not to Turn?

Back in the dark days of instrument flying, when VOR and DME were still sketches on some engineer's luncheon napkin, letting down for an approach was an uncertain process. The only way a pilot could be sure of his position was to fly over the top of a navaid, usually a low-frequency radio range or an NDB. When the tone nulled or the needle swung, the pilot knew, at least for the moment, exactly where he was.

Timing fix-to-fix was an accurate way to dead reckon along an airway but not nearly accurate enough to punch through an undercast for the approach. For that, the airplane had to again overtop a fix near the airport, then get turned around and aligned on a course that lead to the runway. That "turning around" is the origin of the modern procedure turn.

These days, radar vectoring has made the procedure turn all but extinct. At some airports, major terminals and feeders, for example, it's never done or even allowed. Take the plates for Los Angeles International, for example. Of 16 approaches available, not one has a procedure turn. The mere thought of a pilot trying one in such congested airspace is terrifying enough to keep them from being depicted, even for loss of comm purposes. At outlying airports where radar coverage is poor or non-existent, a procedure turn is usually charted but even at that, it's often only a last ditch means of getting into the approach. Where they exist—and they usually do—no-procedure-turn transition routes are the most expedient method to get aligned with the final approach course.

Who Needs 'Em?

So why are procedure turns depicted on so many approach plates? Excepting the airports where they're the only way to fly the approach, procedure turns are charted chiefly as insurance against loss of radar and communications. They give you a means to get on the ground when all else fails. Unfortunately, because they're on so many charts where they're never executed, procedure turns are a source of considerable confusion and the subject of the occasional hanger argument between pilots discussing the finer points of IFR flying.

Approach plates show three kinds of procedure turns. The commonest might be called a standard procedure turn. It's the familiar 45-180 degree barbed icon on NOS charts or, on Jepps, the full procedure turn track. If there's not enough protected airspace for a standard procedure turn, the approach designer might pick the holding-pattern type procedure turn, which is shown as a bold race track on both types of plates. Holding-pattern procedure turns are often (but not always) located over the final approach fix on a non-precision approach or over a LOM if on an ILS.

The rarest PT is the so-called teardrop. Teardrops are used when two nav facilities aren't colocated and a course reversal must connect an offset outbound course with the inbound approach course. Whenever they're charted, teardrop procedure turns must be flown exactly as depicted.

What the Regs Say

The FARs and their interpretive cousin, the AIM, shed more smoke than light on the subject of procedure turns. FAR 97.3 (p) defines procedure turns as "the maneuver prescribed when it is necessary to reverse direction to establish the aircraft on an intermediate or final approach course." The outbound course, direction of turn, distance within which the turn must be completed and minimum altitude are specified but the point at which the turn commences and the type and rate of turn are up to the pilot.

The reg seems to be saying do a procedure turn when you have to reverse direction but perform it at a rate that suits you. By implication then, no procedure turn is necessary when no course reversal is necessary. The AIM, however, doesn't seem to agree. It says the PT is a "required maneuver" except in these circumstances: when being radar vectored; where the symbol NoPT appears; where a holding pattern is published in lieu of a procedure turn or where the procedure turn is otherwise not authorized.

All this may seem like angels on the head of a pin and it would be except that there are some instances when it's not apparent from the chart just what the pilot is supposed to do or why. Some approaches have transitions that direct the pilot either right to the final approach fix or to a course that aligns with the intermediate or final segment. The way the AIM tells it, if a procedure turn is depicted and the transition you're on isn't labeled NoPT, you're supposed to fly the turn, whether you need it for course reversal and/or descent or not.

Take the VOR 7 to Burbank, California, shown on the next page. Suppose you were cleared for the approach via direct to GINNA intersection with a crossing restriction of 5,000 feet or above. Naturally, you'd arrive at GINNA, pick up the intermediate segment and fly it inbound. At SUANA, you could descend to 3,500 feet and continue inbound. Or could you? Not according to the AIM. You weren't vectored and you didn't arrive via a NoPT transition. So, absurd as it seems, even though you're aligned with the course and don't need to lose altitude, you're supposed to take a turn around the racetrack before continuing inbound.

Note that the two NoPT transition routes leading into the approach have the same 5,000 foot minimum altitudes as the route from GINNA. This leads to the obvious question: should that route have been labeled NoPT? The answer is yes. It was simply overlooked and the transition has since been corrected. There is, of course, no way for a pilot to know this.

You might argue that no PT is necessary because this approach has a holding pattern in lieu of a procedure turn. Extending that logic shows how muddled the AIM can be. If it were true that no PT is to be made whenever there's a holding pattern in lieu of the turn, you'd turn only when a standard PT or teardrop is depicted. What the AIM really means is that you're not to do a *standard procedure turn* when a holding-pattern type turn is depicted in its place.

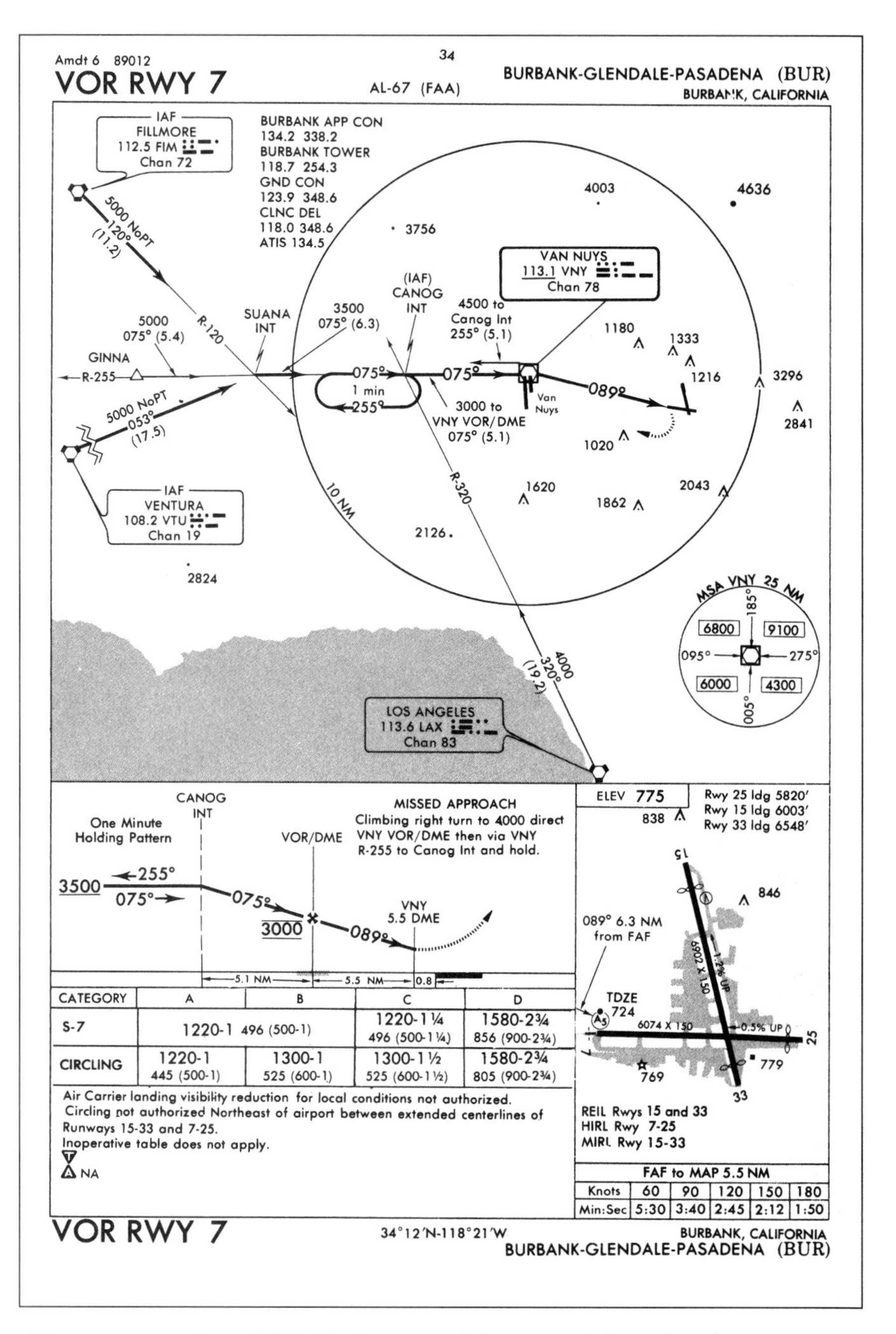

CATEGORY	A	B	C	D
S-7	1220-1 496 (500-1)		1220-1¼ 496 (500-1¼)	1580-2¾ 856 (900-2¾)
CIRCLING	1220-1 445 (500-1)	1300-1 525 (600-1)	1300-1½ 525 (600-1½)	1580-2¾ 805 (900-2¾)

Air Carrier landing visibility reduction for local conditions not authorized.
Circling not authorized Northeast of airport between extended centerlines of Runways 15-33 and 7-25.
Inoperative table does not apply.

FAF to MAP 5.5 NM					
Knots	60	90	120	150	180
Min:Sec	5:30	3:40	2:45	2:12	1:50

The transition from GINNA shown on this approach has since been marked NoPT, just as it should be.

Why not straight in?

Another approach that illustrates the difference between what pilots are supposed to do and what they really do is the NDB-A to Rangeley, Maine, shown on the next page. There are two transition routes, one from Hornebrook NDB another from Berlin VOR. Neither is a NoPT route. The Berlin transition is almost perfectly aligned with the final approach course. You'd have to asleep at the yoke to miss picking up the inbound bearing while on the transition. In this case, it's easy to see why the PT is required but an argument can be made that it shouldn't be.

The transition keeps you at 4,800 feet so the procedure turn is useful to descend down to the 3,500 foot FAF crossing altitude. But remember, the FAF crossing altitude is a minimum. You can be higher if you want, although nothing the FAA has written down says just how much higher.

So, if you can be higher at the FAF, why not dump it down to the MDA as you pass Rangeley beacon on the inbound transition, skipping the PT entirely? If you wanted to arrive at MDA one mile before the missed approach point, a descent from 4,800 feet to 2,440 feet would require a rate of 870 feet per minute; hardly unreasonable for a non-precision approach. The problem here—and another reason you're legally required to do the PT—is that this approach, as well as every other, is designed according to the TERPS manual, and not the way pilots really fly their airplanes.

According to TERPS, the optimum descent gradient for an NDB approach is 300 feet per mile, the maximum is 400 feet. For a category A aircraft, that works out to 450 and 600 feet per minute, respectively. These rates are far more leisurely than most of us would ever use. But as with every other government regulation, TERPS works to the lowest common denominator. In doing so, it has to accommodate everything from Cessna 172s to Lears. The people who wrote TERPS realize that most pilots will exceed the optimum gradient so they built wide safety margins into approach procedures. By requiring the PT, there's no way a pilot can stretch the margins.

Another consideration that might lead you to bag the procedure turn is what the controller expects you to do. Let's use the Rangeley example again. Suppose you're inbound on the transition and maybe picking up ice. You don't want hang around in the clouds any longer than absolutely necessary so you tell the controller you're going to skip the turn and go straight in. In all likelihood, he'll clear you for the approach without reminding you that AIM 371 says the PT is required. If all goes well and you land without incident, that'll probably be the end of it. Splash into the lake short of the airport, however, and your PT-less

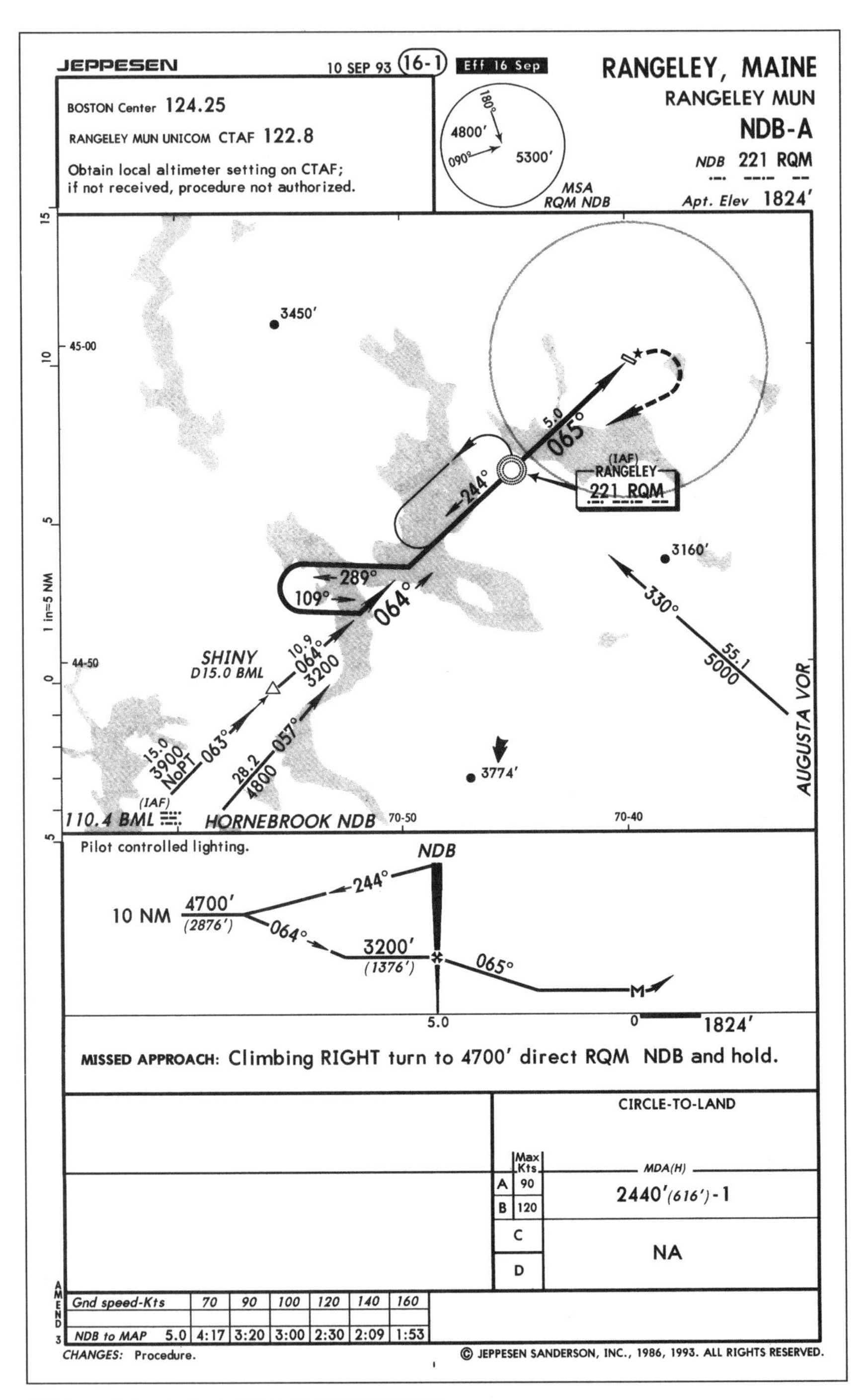
JEPPESEN
10 SEP 93 (16-1) Eff 16 Sep
RANGELEY, MAINE
RANGELEY MUN
NDB-A
NDB 221 RQM
Apt. Elev 1824'
BOSTON Center 124.25
RANGELEY MUN UNICOM CTAF 122.8
Obtain local altimeter setting on CTAF; if not received, procedure not authorized.
180°
4800'
090°
5300'
MSA RQM NDB
3450'
45-00
44-50
3160'
3774'
(IAF) RANGELEY 221 RQM
5.0
065°
244°
289°
109°
064°
SHINY D15.0 BML
10.9 064° 3200
15.0 3900 NoPT 063°
28.2 4800 057°
330° 55.1 5000
AUGUSTA VOR
(IAF) 110.4 BML
HORNEBROOK NDB
70-50
70-40
1 in=5 NM
Pilot controlled lighting.
NDB
10 NM
4700' (2876')
244°
064°
3200' (1376')
065°
5.0
0
1824'
MISSED APPROACH: Climbing RIGHT turn to 4700' direct RQM NDB and hold.
CIRCLE-TO-LAND
Max Kts
MDA(H)
A 90
B 120
2440'(616')-1
C
D
NA
Gnd speed-Kts 70 90 100 120 140 160
NDB to MAP 5.0 4:17 3:20 3:00 2:30 2:09 1:53
AMEND 3
CHANGES: Procedure.
© JEPPESEN SANDERSON, INC., 1986, 1993. ALL RIGHTS RESERVED.

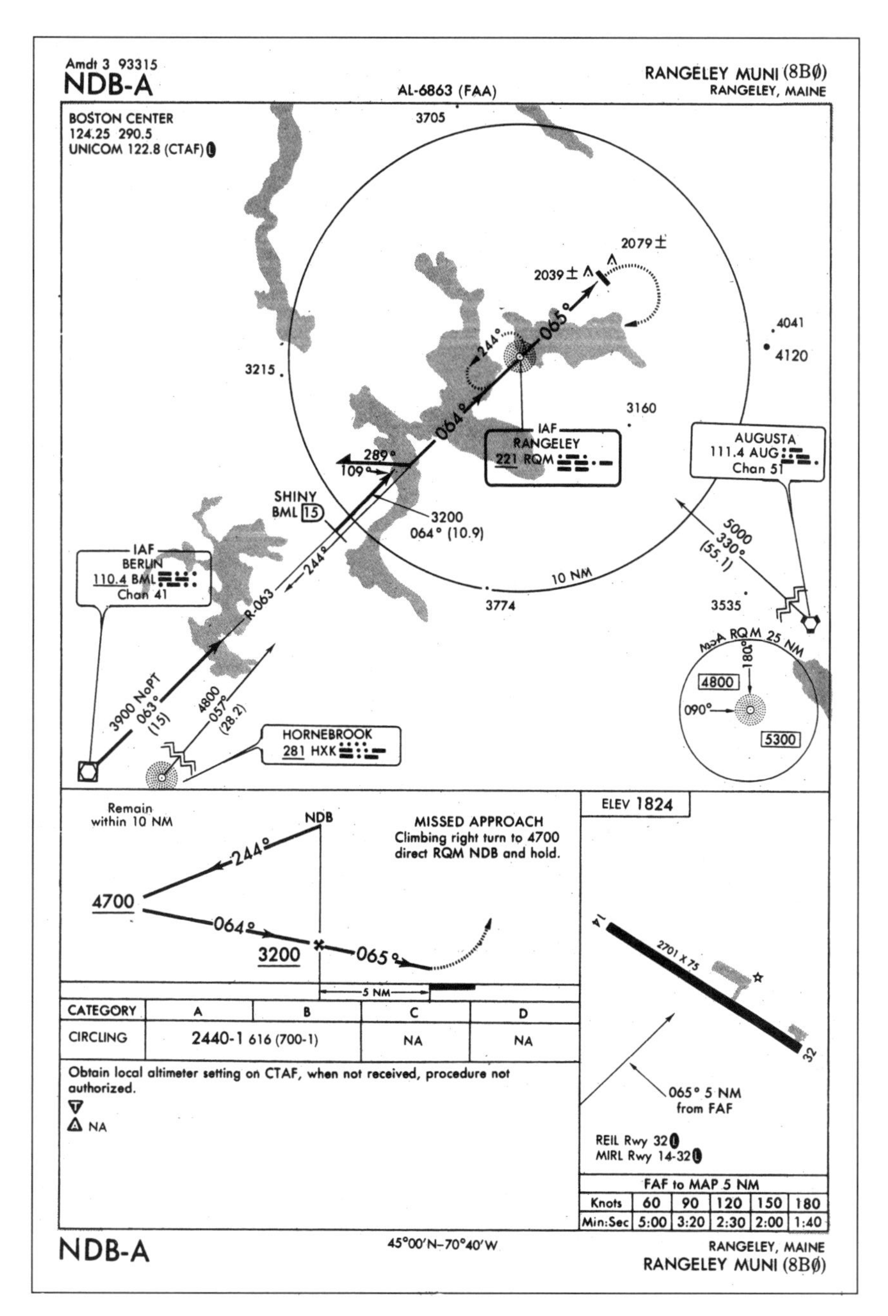

CATEGORY	A	B	C	D
CIRCLING	2440-1 616 (700-1)		NA	NA

Obtain local altimeter setting on CTAF, when not received, procedure not authorized.

FAF to MAP 5 NM					
Knots	60	90	120	150	180
Min:Sec	5:00	3:20	2:30	2:00	1:40

Both the Berlin and Hornbrook transitions are almost straight-in, but neither is a NoPT route. It may seem inconvenient, but there is a reason for it: It has to do with TERPS procedures.

approach may be the subject of an uncomfortable conversation with the FAA.

The situation is different for a pilot being vectored into the approach. In this case, the AIM is clear: the pilot is relieved of having to do the procedure turn. That doesn't mean you can't do one, you're just not required to. If you want the turn to lose altitude or you aren't satisfied with your alignment, ask for a procedure turn or another vector. Barring conflicting traffic, it'll probably be approved. Don't mistake being vectored with being in radar contact. If you're in radar contact, the controller will simply watch you fly the approach. If the PT is required and you skip it, nothing will be said...unless there's a separation bust or some other surprise, in which case you'll get a free demonstration of the neat way that ATC stores radar data.

Cutting the Corner

Most of fly the 45-180 degree procedure turn, either because that's all our instructors taught us or because we're too lazy to try anything different. But as FAR 97.3 suggests, the pilot can perform the standard course reversal any way he pleases. The only proviso is that the pilot must perform the turn on the maneuvering side of the course and within the distance specified on the plate; usually ten miles but as few as five or as many as 15 miles.

For a standard PT (not a holding pattern or teardrop) you won't find timing, rate or direction of turn spelled out by the FAA. If you want to split-S your way through the turn, have at it, so long as the vis is good enough for aerobatics. The standard 45-180 PT is normally made in the direction opposite the first turn or away from the airport. But it doesn't have to be. It's your prerogative to turn towards the airport, if that makes more sense. Similarly, if the wind direction dictates more or less than a minute on the outbound 45 degree turn, adjust the time to suit the conditions.

Two other PT methods are quicker. The 40-second turn is done with a 45 degree turn from the outbound followed by a sweeping inbound turn that, with any luck, will put you square on the inbound course without having to fly a short straight leg, as with the 45-180. In no wind, the outbound is simply 40-seconds. But there's always wind, so you'll have to adjust the time to allow for it by remembering the wind correction that kept you on the outbound course. If your turn is downwind, subtract one second for each degree of crab angle on the outbound, if upwind, add one second for each degree of crab.

The 90-270 turn is the fastest way to turn around. It requires no timing and will work in high winds, so long as the 90 degree turn isn't made directly downwind. Simply execute a 90 degree turn (towards the maneuvering side) followed immediately by a 270 in the opposite direction back toward the inbound. To account for crab angle, remember to make the first turn 90 degrees to your heading, not 90 degrees to the published course.

You can begin your PT anywhere you like, so long as it's past the outbound procedure turn fix. That's often the FAF, too, but not always. The only requirement is to stay within the 5, 10 or 15 miles specified on the plate. Most pilots do this by timing two minutes outbound if the fix is off the airport, three if it's on the airport. Shorten or lengthen the outbound as necessary to compensate for winds or, if it's available, use DME to stay inside the range limit and skip the timing altogether.

Let's take a slightly different look at procedure turns. The real problem with these beasties is that many pilots just aren't sure if they're supposed to fly one in a given situation.

The following discussion of when and when not to make a procedure turn was prompted by reader feedback to a quiz that appeared in IFR several months ago.

Procedure Turns Revisited

Recently, the mail brought a handful of letters taking us to task for this bold declaration, which appeared in a 1993 quiz answers section: "There's no regulatory requirement to commence an approach at an IAF." Seems innocent enough. But judging by the mail we received, not to mention the continual trickle of questions we hear on this topic, it's clear that pilots are still a little confused about this question: When must you make a procedure turn and when should you not? And how are you supposed to know the difference?

We'll get to the regulatory argument eventually, but for now, let's just say this: *Who cares?* The FARs on this subject are so vague that we don't find a lot of guidance. Our view is that it's far more important to understand the operational need for the procedure turn than it is to worry about letter-perfect compliance or what some obscure paragraph in TERPs means. More on that later.

Turn or Not?

Our quiz was prompted by the crash of a commuter airliner in Anniston, Alabama in which the crew skipped the procedure turn on an ILS, became confused about the aircraft's true position, and crashed beyond the airport. Just to set the record straight, we erroneously reported that aircraft turned onto the ILS 5 localizer just inside the marker, after skipping the procedure turn. In fact, it never got established on the front course localizer at all, but maneuvered north of the airport, crossing the extended runway centerline (the departure end) of runway 5, eventually crashing north of the airport.

In any case, the crew was confused about whether they were on radar vectors to the localizer or the full approach, which would have required a procedure turn in order to align with the localizer inbound. This sort of confusion is very common, especially among pilots who are accustomed to getting vectors to final but don't fly in a non-radar environment much. It's aggravated by traditional training, which tends to focus on the mile-a-minute pace of flying IFR into terminals, at the expense of operating in the outback, where ATC's services are delivered via pay phone, if at all.

How to know, then, when the PT is required and when not? It's all in the AIM, in section 5-48. In brief, the PT is prescribed "when it is necessary to reverse direction to establish the aircraft inbound on an intermediate or final approach course." The AIM goes on to say that the PT is "required" except when the NoPT symbol is shown on the chart, when radar vectoring is provided, when a holding pattern is published in lieu of a procedure turn or when the procedure turn is not authorized. There's a fifth exception dealing with timed approaches but it's such a rare occurrence that it's of little concern.

All of this seems simple enough. Yet in the real world, it's sometimes difficult to know if you're on vectors to final or not. The key is in the phraseology. Controllers are required to tell you if you're on vectors, with a phrase similar to this: "Expect the ILS runway 17, radar vectors to the final approach course." You might also be assigned a heading and altitude, to which the controller appends the phrase "radar vectors to the final approach course."

As you approach the airport, the controller will again use a specific phrase that leaves little doubt that you're being vectored. It's a real mouthful and controllers are *required* to say it all: "One Zulu November, you're three miles from FOXXY, turn left heading 150 degrees, maintain 2500 until established on the final approach course, cleared for the ILS 18 approach." (As we've noted before in *The Instrument Pilot's Library*, it's *not* necessary for you to read back the whole thing.)

The Full Approach

For most approaches, then, the controller will tell you once or twice that radar vectors are the plan. In most cases—but not necessarily all cases—

that means no procedure turn. The exception is the famous slam-dunk (more on this in a later chapter) or any other situation in which you, as the pilot, can't align the aircraft to your satisfaction or otherwise feel uncomfortable with the vector.

In a slam-dunk, you may be brought in high, fast and close and if that just won't work, tell the controller you want another vector or, if one exists, a trip around the procedure turn. Many ILSs have a holding-pattern-in-lieu of a PT. If you hit the marker too fast or too high, a turn around the holding pattern will give you time to scrub off the speed and altitude. Just be sure to tell the controller what you're doing and get his approval.

While controllers are required to specifically tell you when you'll be vectored to final, they aren't required to say when the procedure turn is expected, at least not in so many words. If you're flying into an area of limited or poor radar coverage, chances are you'll be issued the full approach. That means either a procedure turn or flying via a transition or feeder route or both. If the transition has a NoPT note, you know what to do. (Or what *not* to do.)

Here's where it gets confusing. Most pilots are so used to radar vectors that they mistakenly *assume* that's what ATC is doing; that's exactly what happened to the commuter crew in Anniston. Again, the clue is in the phraseology. If the controller has no radar coverage or expects you to fly the full approach for some other reason, here's what he or she will say: "Cross the Meriden NDB at or above 4000 feet, cleared for the NDB 36 approach."

The words are as important for what they *don't* say as what they do. There's no mention of radar vectors, just a direct clearance and an altitude. There's no mention of a procedure turn, either. In most cases, the controller won't know or care if the procedure turn is necessary. All he cares about is scribbling your down time on the flight strip so he can get to the next customer. It's up to the pilot to decide if a procedure turn is necessary.

You'll sometimes hear another version of this clearance, something like "cross the VOR at or above 3000, cleared for the approach via the Johnstown transition." This phraseology is not strictly by the book, but it clearly implies the full approach. If an approach clearance is tacked onto a navaid crossing restriction and a transition is required to fly the approach, the controller will assume that you know what to do. He or she won't specifically say.

By the way, if you prefer the full approach or want to fly a transition even in a radar environment, just ask. Most controllers will probably approve it.

Doing the Turn

As far the procedure turn itself goes, it's up to you how to do it. In the case of a standard procedure turn—the barbed-arrow jobs that require a 180-degree turn—you can do it any way you like. The AIM and FARs are at least clear on this point. You can follow the exact track depicted on the plate or cobble up your own method. That means if the barbed arrow depicts a left turn followed by a right turn back to the inbound course, you can get creative and fly a left turn back to the inbound.

In certain wind and weather conditions, we can see why you'd want to do this. Maybe you'd fly into a killer cell if you turned right or maybe the view is better off the left wing. Whatever. The exception to this is a procedural track, such as a holding-pattern-in-lieu of a procedure turn. These are supposed to be flown as published.

All the timing tricks you were taught as an instrument student are optional, too. There's no requirement to time anything. Just make sure you remain on the protected side of the course and within the lateral boundaries given in the profile view; usually within 10 miles of the fix upon which the turn is based, but it varies.

If you have this much latitude in doing the procedure turn, can you then skip it entirely if you're properly aligned and can go straight in? Our view is that there's no specific regulation prohibiting this. As we said in the quiz, Part 91 doesn't specifically address it. FAR 97.3 comes closest by defining a procedure turn prescribed "when it's necessary to reverse direction to establish the aircraft on an intermediate or final approach course." If you're already established on the intermediate, why is the turn necessary? Why can't you just skip it entirely?

The Legal Argument

"FAR 97.3 may appear to give discretion to the pilot but AIM-5-48a certainly does not," writes David Oberbeck, a CFII from California. "While the AIM may not have the force and effect of the FARs, I would suppose the FAA could make a 'careless and reckless' stick if you didn't follow the AIM recommendations."

That's probably true. But our experience with violations suggests that most occur because something went drastically wrong—a separation bust or the pilot bent metal. Absent any other problems, we doubt if the FAA would pursue a violation *purely* on the grounds of a skipped PT. (We couldn't find any enforcement history on this.)

Walt Echwald, a Virginia CFII, argues that the regulatory bite is contained in TERPs and in FAR 91.185, which says in the event of lost comm, a pilot is supposed to proceed to an IAF. "This, in my judgment, affirms that the FAA intent is that an IAF is where it all begins." Further, says Echwald, "this is also set forth in the TERPs manual...and is directive in nature."

TERPs is indeed directive but whether it's a pilot's guide is debatable. It's a manual for designing approaches, not flying them. Echwald does make the good point that "following anything other than the road map provided on the IAP is less than safe." We'll agree with that.

As we implied in the quiz, we're not arguing that you should routinely skip procedure turns or invent your own procedures. But there are circumstances when the regs are sufficiently vague to allow the insertion of common sense. A prime example is a pilot who finds himself established on an intermediate approach segment, properly aligned and at the right altitude, having never crossed the IAF. If you accept that the regs require a PT, you'll turn outbound and fly a few more miles. Otherwise, continue with the approach and land. It's your choice.

The Slam-Dunk and Other Tricks

In the last chapter we briefly mentioned something called the "slam-dunk." We'll get to exactly what that is in this chapter, but for now all you need to know is that it's one of the little tricks controllers use to fit more airplanes into a given chunk of sky than would be possible otherwise.

During training, we learn how important it is to keep a proper, relatively sedate airspeed on final, to make gentle turns, and so forth. Sounds great. In the real world, if you're grinding away in a Skyhawk trying to sneak into a never-ending stream of 737s and MD-80s for an ILS, you can chuck all that out the window unless you want to wait till Christmas.

It's time to bring Ross Russo back for a look at flying approaches in the real world.

Stabilized Approach? Hah!

As a basic IFR technique, a stabilized approach is a great and wondrous thing. However, the concept dates to the early 1940s, when all airplanes flew final at about the same speed (80 knots, give or take). Even the fighters of the day weren't much faster, coming down the chute at just over 100 knots. Mixing up traffic on final was no big deal. It's easy to sort the crayons when they're all the same color.

As the airlines moved from piston engines to turboprops and jets, however, approach speeds started to diverge, from a low of 80 knots, to well over 100 knots. At first, this proved to be but a minor irritant. Controllers had to do a bit of vectoring or the slow guys might have to hold for a minute or two to let the kerosene burners flash by, but it was generally no big deal. Then along came huge increases in traffic, plus the hub-and-spoke system that's standard operating practice today.

Traffic density around some hubs increased exponentially. What used to be a relatively predictable stream of aircraft turned into a schizophrenic torrent that would subside as quickly as it developed. The flash-flood phenomenon has proved difficult for pilots, controllers and airports. If an airport only served air carriers, it wouldn't be so bad; most jets fly approaches at very near the same speed.

Mixing It Up

But what happens when you try to fit an 80-knot Cherokee into that flow of heavy iron? Now you're trying to sort a case of crayons of various sizes and colors. Throw in some weather, ice and thunderstorms and you're sorting in the dark. Not a fun place to be.

Vectors and holds only work so well. Big Sky theory or not, the airspace around most airports is cut up too much to allow controllers to vector airplanes anywhere they'd like. And a Cherokee only holds so much fuel; parking one in a hold until the rush subsides just won't do.

For GA pilots, this has resulted in a head-long thrust into the past. To survive the traffic mix of the 90s, we have to use techniques from the 30s, meaning that we're often asked to match speeds with the big guys and speed up or slow down on final, thus trashing the concept of a stabilized approach at a standard airspeed.

Is this a problem? Not really, except that most of us were never trained to fly anything but a stabilized approach and we sometimes think it's unsafe to do anything else. Most instructors teach students to cross the final approach fix with the aircraft in the landing configuration and at the final approach speed. While that works for the Boeing and Douglas crowd at 130 knots, it doesn't help the poor slug in a 172 who's burning up the final approach course at a blistering 70 knots with a Lear three miles in trail.

Thankfully, controllers are a devious lot. Their charter is to move metal (albeit safely), and move metal they will. In response to the hub-and-spoke dilemma, they've perfected three techniques that allow the little guys (including turboprops) to slip into the Conga line of jets. If you've done any flying around airports with a high volume of airline traffic, then you've probably seen at least one of these, if not all three: the tight turn-on, the blazing final, or the slam-dunk.

Unfortunately, none of these techniques are compatible with the classic, stabilized approach. Once again, the real world proves more harsh than the one your CFII prepared you to face.

The Tight Turn On

Of the three techniques, the tight turn-on is perhaps the easiest for the

The Stabilized Approach: How The Idea Was Born

It takes a certain courage to challenge the prevailing wisdom. At a time when most pilots were making full-stall, three-point landings in the DC-3 and using a constantly decreasing airspeed on final to achieve this, it took a true zealot to propose a stabilized airspeed final followed by a wheel landing. That's exactly what Ralph Johnson did and he's generally recognized as the inventer of the stabilized approach.

Johnson was United Airlines' chief test pilot back in the 1930s when he began exploring the benefits of the stabilized approach. In those days, a smooth landing and a short roll out was considered the mark of a true pro. Most pilots achieved it by the rather tricky method of a slow power reduction down final, hitting a target airspeed at some predetermined point.

Johnson argued that a stabilized approach, followed by a wheel landing would yield equal performance with less pilot stress. His technique was simple: Fly the DC-3 at a constant 90 MPH on final, use the elevators to control the rate of descent and the throttles to control the airspeed. When the mains touched the runway, ease forward on the yoke, close the throttles, and lower the tail.

Johnson was both an accomplished pilot and an engineer so he conducted a series of experiments to prove his theories. At United's test facilities, he measured the impact of full-stall landings versus wheel landings. Wheel landings proved easier on the tires and touching down at a descent rate of 400 feet per minute was equal to a static drop of only 8.2 inches. Tests also showed that the stabilized approach resulted in landing distances that were identical to full-stall approaches. Johnson provided the proof that turned the industry around and his lasting legacy—the stabilized approach—remains the accepted way to fly an airplane down the final approach course. —*J.R.R.*

pilot. When ATC is providing vectors to final, the controllers are required to issue a heading that will allow the pilot to intercept the final approach course at an angle of roughly 30 degrees.

Depending on the weather, that intercept is supposed to occur two to three miles outside an imaginary point called the approach gate. On an ILS, the gate is about a mile outside of the marker or, if there's no marker, the fix that serves as the non-precision FAF. If the weather is poor—reported ceiling less than 500 feet above the local minimum vectoring altitude—the controller will try for a vector that's no closer than two miles outside the gate. That makes sense. With poorer weather conditions, the pilot could certainly use more time on final to get stabilized.

There's a way to cut corners here. The pilot can request a tight turn-on (or words to that effect). It's a good tool. If a pilot is familiar with an approach and proficient at speed management, there's no need to fly an additional two miles on final. Of course, some controllers will tell you that the radar display isn't good enough for that kind of accuracy but that's likely to vary with facility.

The real challenge comes when the controller solicits the tight turn. Is this 100 percent kosher? Not really, but it happens. Most controllers are highly motivated to move metal and if a tight turn-on can get you in five or ten minutes earlier, that's what they'll shoot for. They're trying to be helpful. In most cases it works. But not always.

Consider this conversation between a regional commuter and approach control. The tower at the destination field had closed and another commuter had just landed but failed to cancel IFR with the approach controller. The field was right at mins, so the commuter couldn't cancel until after landing.

The second commuter was forced to go around while the controller called airport security and had them drive the runway. Yes, there was an XYZ commuter on the ramp, but there was no way to make sure it was the *right* XYZ commuter.

As the second commuter was being vectored on the downwind, the controller reported that the runway was clear and asked if the regional could take a tight turn-on to final. The captain responded, "It's late, we've been flying all day, we're tired, and the weather is right at minimums; we'll take a nice and easy turn-on, please." A good call. Just remember, it's your choice, not the controller's.

If you do accept the tight turn-on, the big thing to worry about is getting behind the airplane. You're going to have less time to configure, you may have to go down and slow down at the same time, while simultaneously maneuvering to intercept the final. This can really hike up the workload during a critical phase of flight.

While the tight turn-on can certainly fill your plate during the first segment of the approach, there is a bright side. Once you're established, you can usually cruise down the beam at your normal approach speed. Except for a few hectic minutes at the outset, you can still end up with a stabilized approach.

Again, it's your choice. If you're fresh and sharp and up to the intense workload the tight turn-on will require, have at it. Otherwise, reject the offer and ask for vectors well outside the gate.

The Blazing Final

How often have you heard a controller ask, "What speed can you give me on final?" I know the answer to that one. I'm sure you do too. If you expect to get a reserved slot in the queue, you'd better say that you can fly anything the controller wants. My personal technique is to say that I can maintain 120 knots indicated until I'm over the approach lights. That usually does the trick.

The critical part is letting the controller know when you'll slow down. Here's a story that illustrates why some controllers are hesitant to trust you with a blazing final. Picture an airport with a great deal of air carrier traffic jockeying for position on the ILS. Naturally, there are always a few slower aircraft as well. On this particular day, the controller saw a window of opportunity and asked a 172 what airspeed he could deliver on final.

The Cessna signed up for 110 knots. Bingo. The Cessna driver was on his way to the runway and all was right with the world. But not for long. Apparently, the pilot's idea of how long to hold that 110 knots wasn't what the controller had in mind. You could see what was going to happen when the controller asked a DC-9 following the Cessna how *slow* he'd be able to fly final.

As the distance between the jet and the Cessna shrank, the controller asked the 172 pilot for an airspeed call out. Even though he was still miles from the runway, the Cessna had slowed to 80 knots. The DC-9 was sent around and I'm sure the controller vowed never again to trust a flib (friendly little itinerant buddy). *(You may choose a more colorful substitution for "friendly "and "buddy."— Ed.)*

There are two schools of thought about when to slow to final-approach speed. Some pilots prefer to slow down at about a mile or two from the threshold; others like to make a single power reduction and decelerate continually to the flare, once the runway is in sight.

The advantage of slowing while still some distance from the runway is that it allows at least a semblance of a stabilized approach. The disadvantage is that the momentum of a decelerating aircraft must be stopped at the target airspeed, by the addition of power, further complicating the airspeed/descent equation. If you're in IMC, you'll increase your workload just as you're approaching DH.

On the other hand, the constant deceleration of pulling the throttles back over the approach lights eliminates the need to stabilize at an intermediate speed. The price you'll pay is a significant change in control and trim pressures while transitioning to the visual environment. In low vis or at night, this can be disconcerting, to say the least.

I tend to fly fast right up until I can glide safely to the runway because that's the way I learned to fly gliders. In order to have a bit of "money in the bank," gliders approach at a relatively high airspeed. I'd suggest you go out and practice both techniques, then use the one that suits you. With proper training and experience, either will suffice.

The Slam Dunk

This is the all-time worst way to fly an approach. For some reason, the controller has you close to the final approach fix, but you're a couple of thousand feet higher than the published glideslope intercept altitude. Again, in an attempt to be helpful, the controller issues an approach clearance. (He doesn't want to delay you, after all.)

This presents the pilot with a daunting challenge. All the forces of nature are aligned against him. Stabilized approach? Forget it. You're high, so you're going to have to stay faster than normal to lose the altitude; either that or risk premature cylinder work by chopping the throttles for a rapid descent at some reasonable airspeed. Then there's the passengers' ears to consider.

In this scenario, you're forced to accomplish a more complex task in less time than normal. Approach the slam-dunk with extreme caution. If it doesn't feel right for any reason, reject it and get proper vectors at the correct altitude.

You can usually tell when a slam-dunk is in your future. At some airports, because of traffic considerations, it's almost standard procedure when approaching from certain directions. Slick airplanes like Mooneys and Bonanzas are particularly susceptible because controllers mistakenly assume that these airplanes can descend in the same distance that a Cherokee or a Cessna can.

One way to manage the slam-dunk is to keep accurate position awareness when being vectored. Plan ahead. If you're close in to the final and still high, start a gradual slowdown to gear and flap speeds so you can dirty up as necessary. You'll then have the *option* of the rapid descent, if you want to give it a try. If you decide to descend clean, you'll have to bleed off the airspeed and reconfigure later on, perhaps inside the final approach fix. Nothing wrong with that, as long as you can handle the workload.

Nonetheless, even if you're super proficient, there are limits. There's an old story about a controller requesting a slam-dunk from a grizzled old airline Captain. ATC asks if the pilot can make a descent of 10,000 feet in the next three miles.

"I can," growls the four-striper, "but I can't take the airplane with me."

Training for It

Just to illustrate what's possible, let me describe a technique we use in the Air Force. Around the mid-1980s, fighter pilots, a group not known for tolerant attitudes towards ATC, realized that the separation standards applied during approaches limited the ability to recover aircraft to the home drome. We'd been flying trail departures for years—a procedure whereby departing fighters would keep from swapping paint by using constant airspeeds, constant power settings, and timing.

Takeoffs were at 20-second intervals and all subsequent turns were in increments of 20 seconds (number two would turn 20 seconds after the leader, number three would turn 40 seconds after the leader, etc.). We decided to apply the same procedures to approaches. The result was a technique that combines the tight turn-on, blazing final, and slam-dunk. It's called ASLAR (accelerated surge launch and recovery).

It begins when a flight of two fighters depart the IAF within plus or minus 20 seconds of the approach clearance time. So much for the tight turn-on. Next, they descend at 300 knots (slam-dunk) until they reach the DRAG point. This is where the leader tells the wingman to drag and confirms the altimeter setting. The wingie reduces his power to a specific RPM and opens his speed brakes. Decelerating through 250 knots he lowers the gear and stabilizes at 180 knots (blazing final).

The flight leader executes these exact same procedures at the DECEL point. This puts the leader roughly 1.5 miles in front of his wingman. Each pilot slows to his final approach speed at the FAS point—usually two miles on final.

The procedure works. But it requires special training for both the pilots and controllers. And therein lies the lesson for us flib drivers. (You wondered how I'd connect this with Cherokees, I'll bet.)

As I said before, there's nothing inherently dangerous about either a tight turn-on, blazing final, or slam-dunk, although they are progressively more difficult. The key is finding a procedure that will work for you and your airplane and training to stay current.

It's still a matter of flying an approach by the numbers. The only thing that changes is how long you stabilize at those numbers. Also, you have to be ready to pass up an offer of expeditious handling if you're not comfortable with it. The controller will probably be trying to help but ATC has no clue of what you or your airplane can handle. Don't be intimidated into trying to comply with everything the controller asks of you.

Practice, Practice

Remember when you were getting ready for your private pilot checkride and you spent all that time practicing short- and soft-field takeoffs and landings? How many times have you had to make an honest-to-goodness short- or soft-field landing, let alone over a 50-foot obstacle? I'm not saying that these skills aren't valuable. I am saying that preparing for a tight turn-on, blazing final, or slam-dunk is at least of equal importance.

I'm not suggesting another requirement tacked onto the instrument checkride. But any instructor worth his students' sweat should be preparing his charges for the real world of shooting an approach at a crowded airport.

Flying DME Arcs

Among the more difficult of approaches are those involving DME arcs. While it's not necessary to be as precise in tracking the arc as in tracking a localizer and glideslope, the DME arc is a tough one to fly.

This is because, unlike an ILS or a straightforward non-precision approach, the DME arc represents a constantly changing situation for the pilot to keep up with. Straight-line approaches allow the pilot to set up on a heading, then concentrate on maintaining it. Not so with the DME arc: Your reference heading is changing constantly, and you must be able to follow the arc and still arrive at a specific point in space.

This chapter presents three methods for tracking DME arcs, along with a walk-through of two approaches that have them.

Mastering the Arc

The use of DME arcs in many instrument approaches gives air traffic controllers additional flexibility by freeing up airspace over navaids and establishes two or more additional initial approach fixes in the procedure. In the Instrument Flying Handbook (AC 61-27C), the FAA tells us that unless we're highly proficient in flying arc procedures, DME arcs should only be flown in IMC when a radio magnetic indicator (RMI) is available. We believe any proficient instrument pilot should be able to fly an arc as easily as any other type of approach with or without an RMI.

Arc to Runway

Arc approaches don't always use a VOR facility located on the same airport as the approach procedure. For example, the DME arc to

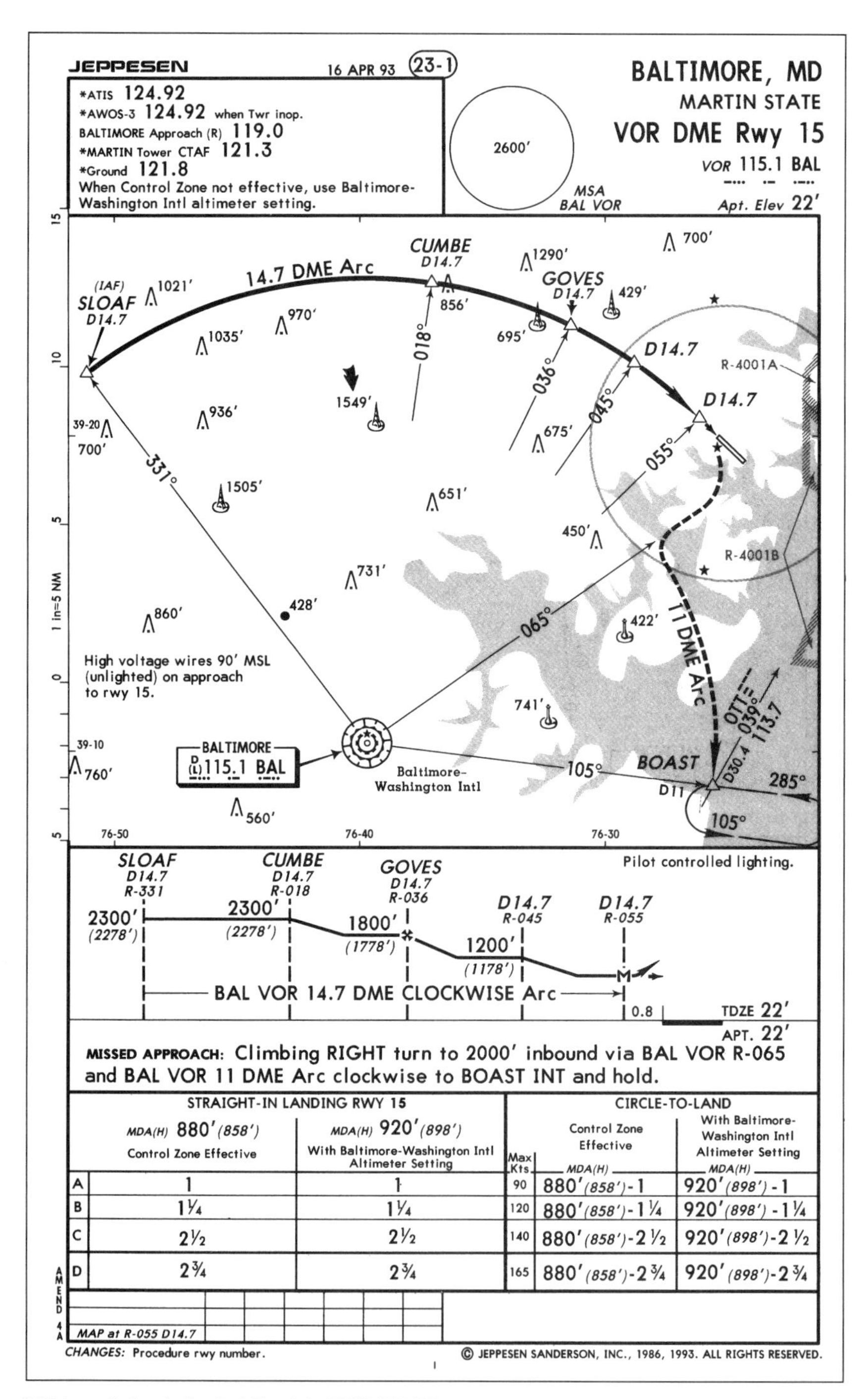
JEPPESEN
16 APR 93
23-1
BALTIMORE, MD
MARTIN STATE
VOR DME Rwy 15
VOR 115.1 BAL
Apt. Elev 22'
*ATIS 124.92
*AWOS-3 124.92 when Twr inop.
BALTIMORE Approach (R) 119.0
*MARTIN Tower CTAF 121.3
*Ground 121.8
When Control Zone not effective, use Baltimore-Washington Intl altimeter setting.
2600'
MSA BAL VOR
(IAF) SLOAF D14.7
14.7 DME Arc
CUMBE D14.7
GOVES D14.7
D14.7
D14.7
R-4001A
R-4001B
018°
036°
045°
055°
331°
065°
105°
285°
11 DME Arc
OTT 039° 113.7
D30.4
BOAST D11
BALTIMORE 115.1 BAL
Baltimore-Washington Intl
High voltage wires 90' MSL (unlighted) on approach to rwy 15.
1 in=5 NM
39-20
39-10
76-50
76-40
76-30
Pilot controlled lighting.
SLOAF D14.7 R-331
CUMBE D14.7 R-018
GOVES D14.7 R-036
D14.7 R-045
D14.7 R-055
2300' (2278')
2300' (2278')
1800' (1778')
1200' (1178')
BAL VOR 14.7 DME CLOCKWISE Arc
0.8
TDZE 22'
APT. 22'
MISSED APPROACH: Climbing RIGHT turn to 2000' inbound via BAL VOR R-065 and BAL VOR 11 DME Arc clockwise to BOAST INT and hold.
STRAIGHT-IN LANDING RWY 15
MDA(H) 880'(858') Control Zone Effective
MDA(H) 920'(898') With Baltimore-Washington Intl Altimeter Setting
CIRCLE-TO-LAND
Control Zone Effective
With Baltimore-Washington Intl Altimeter Setting
A 1 1 90 880'(858')-1 920'(898')-1
B 1¼ 1¼ 120 880'(858')-1¼ 920'(898')-1¼
C 2½ 2½ 140 880'(858')-2½ 920'(898')-2½
D 2¾ 2¾ 165 880'(858')-2¾ 920'(898')-2¾
MAP at R-055 D14.7
CHANGES: Procedure rwy number.
© JEPPESEN SANDERSON, INC., 1986, 1993. ALL RIGHTS RESERVED.

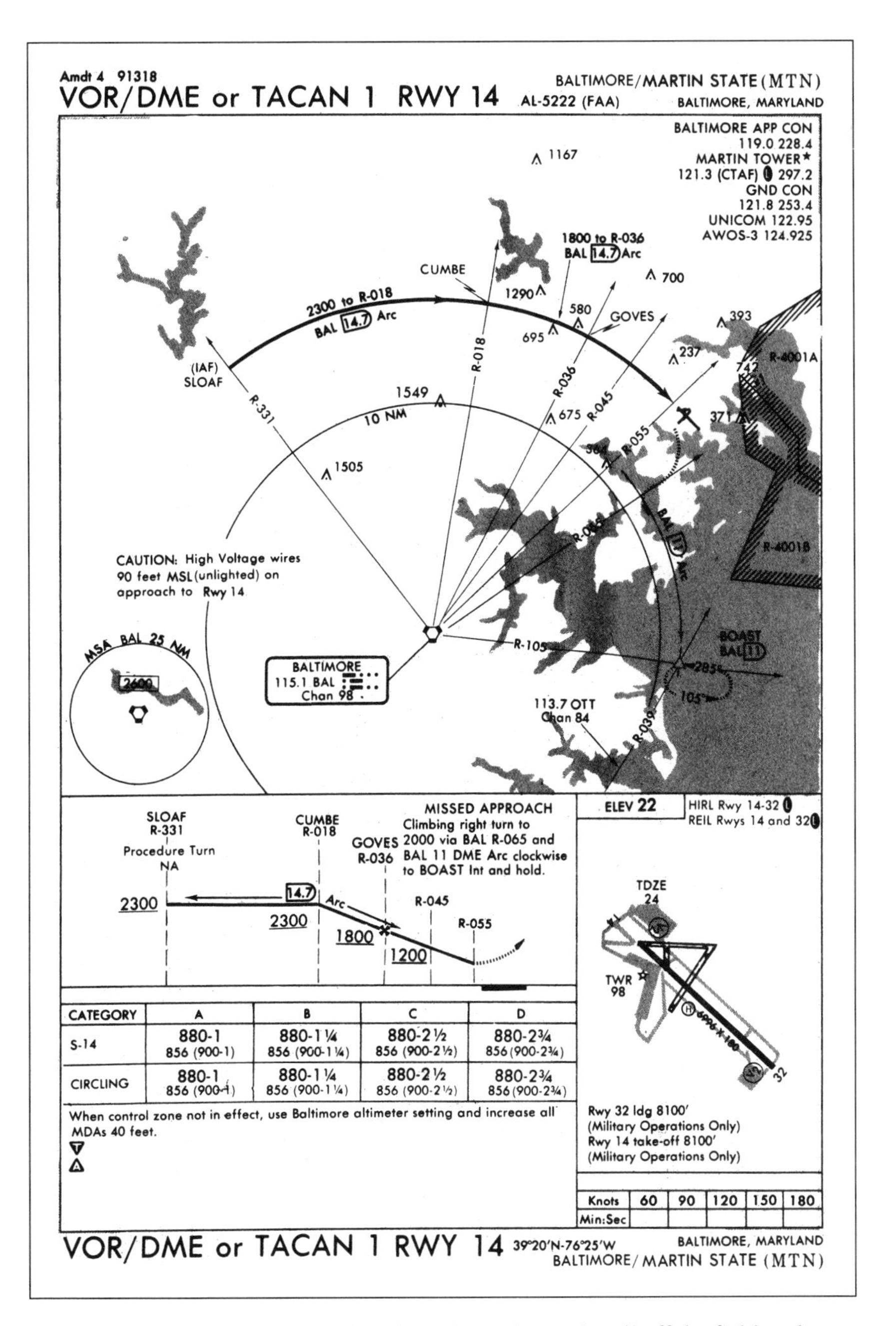

This procedure is unusual in that the VOR is located well off the field and you must fly a continuous arc to the runway. Even the missed approach involves flying a DME arc. (The runway designation recently changed from 14 to 15.)

Runway 14 at Martin State (pp 204-205) uses the Baltimore Vortac and the arc is flown all the way to the runway. There is also an NDB approach to this runway with an MDA 200 feet lower, but there could be circumstances where the NDB is unusable and you need to fly the arc.

Approximately 75 percent of the instrument pilots we've flown with don't know the obstacle clearance on a DME arc. An arc is the same width as an airway, which means the minimum altitude on the chart is protected four nautical miles either side of the centerline.

In the case of the Martin State procedure, you can safely fly the arc up to four nautical miles to either side. But, would you see and safely make the runway if you came roaring toward the airport three miles to either side of the arc with the weather at minimums? It isn't likely, so let's go to work assuming we don't have an RMI.

Three Methods

Listed below are three methods of flying a DME arc. Feel free to use whichever method or combination of methods that work best for you. Refer to the ILS Runway 5 at Anniston, Alabama (pp 208-209). In the first method, review the chart and estimate the first heading you'll fly when intercepting the arc from the 276 radial, which should be 180°.

Turn to 180 and monitor the DME. If the DME increases, turn left 10° and note the distance. If the DME still increases, turn another 10° left. If it decreases, turn 10° right. This is called bracketing and you must change heading to remain within the limits of the arc. If you have an autopilot, move the heading bug to each new heading before turning. This helps monitor your progress while bracketing the arc.

This method doesn't provide position guidance on any radial while on the arc and could result in disorientation in strong winds. However, it's safe and requires the least workload.

The second method requires constant twisting of the OBS to keep the CDI centered. For a left-hand (counterclockwise) arc, turn to a heading 90 degrees less than the radial at the IAF, which in this case is 186°. For a right-hand (clockwise) arc, you must add 90 degrees to the radial.

As you fly the arc, keep centering the CDI on radials from the station. Each time you center the CDI, fly a heading 90 degrees less than the radial you're crossing for a counterclockwise arc or 90 degrees more than the radial for a clockwise arc. The DME must be carefully monitored and heading changes made as in the first method.

The third method is similar to the second except, after making the initial 90-degree turn toward the arc, you turn the OBS 10 degrees ahead. When the CDI centers, turn 10 degrees toward the station and turn the OBS ahead another 10 degrees. Bracket the DME as in the first method.

The second and third methods provide greater positional awareness and you'll always know how close you are to the inbound radial. More workload is required in constantly changing the OBS. If your nav display doesn't have a 360-degree compass card, you must calculate the 90-degree heading. Whereas, if the display has a 360-degree compass card, simply read the 90-degree point from either side of the card.

How it's Done

Let's review two arc approaches and how to set up for each. We've flown the arc to the Anniston ILS in IMC several times in the past year using the first method. The first time we flew this procedure, we had very strong headwinds and turbulence, so it took quite some time to intercept the localizer. If we had used the second or third methods of arc interception, we would have had a much better appreciation of my groundspeed as we moved slowly around the arc.

ATC radar isn't available below 4000 feet, so you must fly this procedure on your own. The typical clearance is, "Cross the Talladega VOR at 4000, cleared ILS Runway 5 approach. Report established on the 276 radial and the seven-mile arc."

Here's a suggested avionics set-up and management:

- #1 VOR/HSI - IANB localizer 111.5, OBS - 49°.
- #2 VOR - TDG VOR 108.8, DME - Hold, OBS - 195° (unless using second or third method).
- ADF - Bogga LOM 211 kHz.

After crossing TDG, set the #1 VOR to 276 and fly this radial to 6.5 DME in order to lead the turn to intercept the 7.0 DME arc. Turn to 180° and monitor the DME, correcting 10° in either direction depending on DME distance. Reset OBS to the 195-degree lead-in radial. Descend to 3000 feet.

At the first indication of crossing the 195 radial, turn to intercept the localizer. Stop the turn at 94° and hold this heading until you get a positive localizer indication. Reset the #2 VOR to the 174 radial to identify Clarc Intersection.

After passing Clarc, descend to 2200 feet to intercept the glideslope. Reset the #2 VOR to the localizer as back-up and complete the approach as published.

Continuous Arc

Refer to the Martin State procedure. This approach has only one IAF

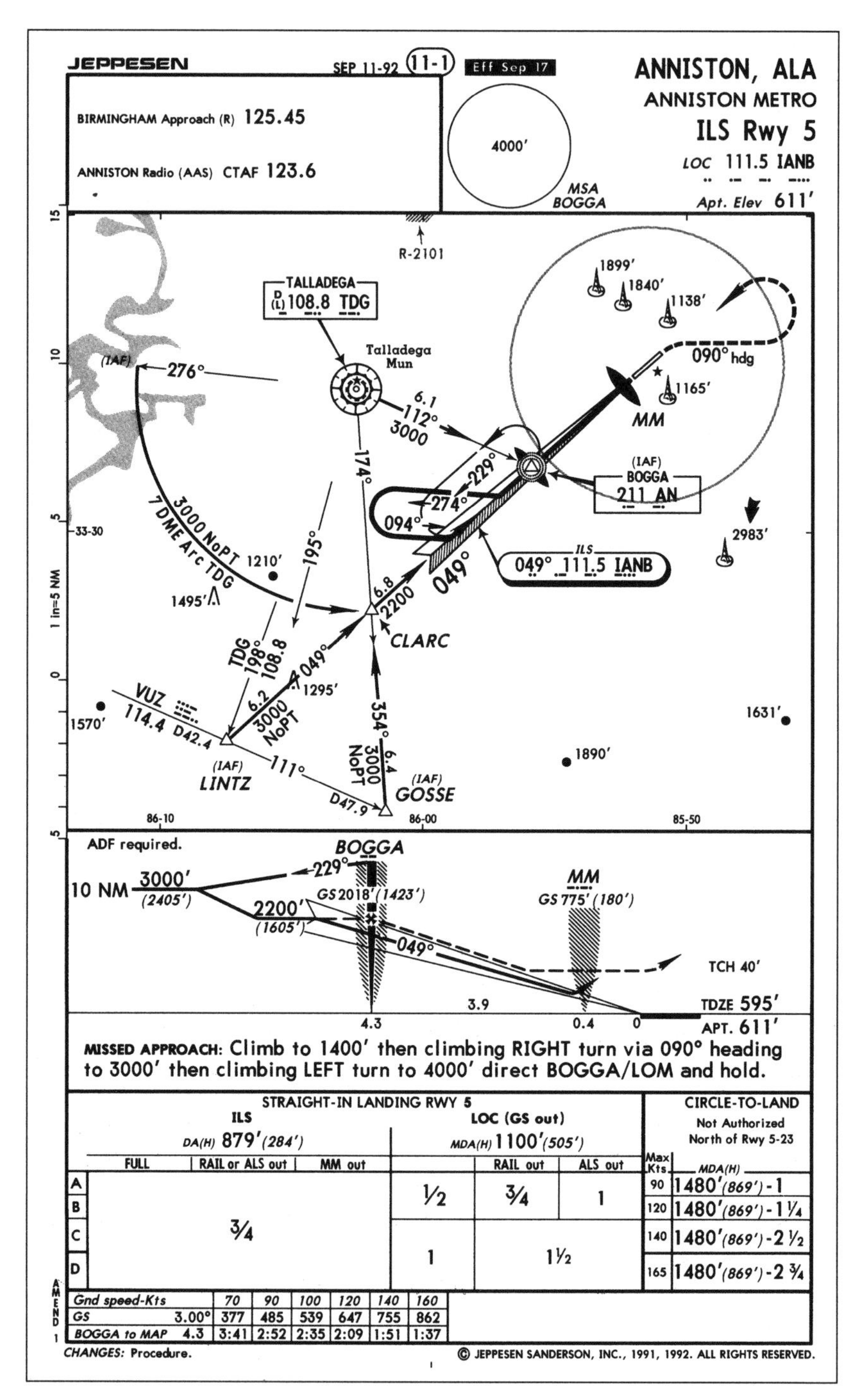
JEPPESEN
SEP 11-92 (11-1)
Eff Sep 17
ANNISTON, ALA
ANNISTON METRO
ILS Rwy 5
LOC 111.5 IANB
Apt. Elev 611'
BIRMINGHAM Approach (R) 125.45
ANNISTON Radio (AAS) CTAF 123.6
4000'
MSA BOGGA
R-2101
TALLADEGA 108.8 TDG
Talladega Mun
6.1
112°
3000
174°
195°
(IAF)
276°
3000 NoPT
7 DME Arc TDG
1899'
1840'
1138'
090° hdg
1165'
MM
229°
274°
094°
(IAF) BOGGA 211 AN
ILS 049° 111.5 IANB
049°
2983'
1210'
1495'
6.8
2200
CLARC
TDG 198° 108.8
049°
1295'
6.2
3000 NoPT
VUZ 114.4 D42.4
1570'
(IAF) LINTZ
111°
D47.9
354°
6.4
3000 NoPT
(IAF) GOSSE
1631'
1890'
33-30
86-10
86-00
85-50
1 in=5 NM
ADF required.
BOGGA
10 NM
3000' (2405')
2200' (1605')
GS 2018' (1423')
MM
GS 775' (180')
TCH 40'
3.9
TDZE 595'
4.3
0.4
0
APT. 611'
MISSED APPROACH: Climb to 1400' then climbing RIGHT turn via 090° heading to 3000' then climbing LEFT turn to 4000' direct BOGGA/LOM and hold.
STRAIGHT-IN LANDING RWY 5
ILS
DA(H) 879' (284')
LOC (GS out)
MDA(H) 1100' (505')
FULL
RAIL or ALS out
MM out
RAIL out
ALS out
A
B
C
D
3/4
1/2
3/4
1
1
1 1/2
CIRCLE-TO-LAND
Not Authorized North of Rwy 5-23
Max Kts
MDA(H)
90 1480' (869') - 1
120 1480' (869') - 1 1/4
140 1480' (869') - 2 1/2
165 1480' (869') - 2 3/4
Gnd speed-Kts 70 90 100 120 140 160
GS 3.00° 377 485 539 647 755 862
BOGGA to MAP 4.3 3:41 2:52 2:35 2:09 1:51 1:37
AMEND 1
CHANGES: Procedure.
© JEPPESEN SANDERSON, INC., 1991, 1992. ALL RIGHTS RESERVED.

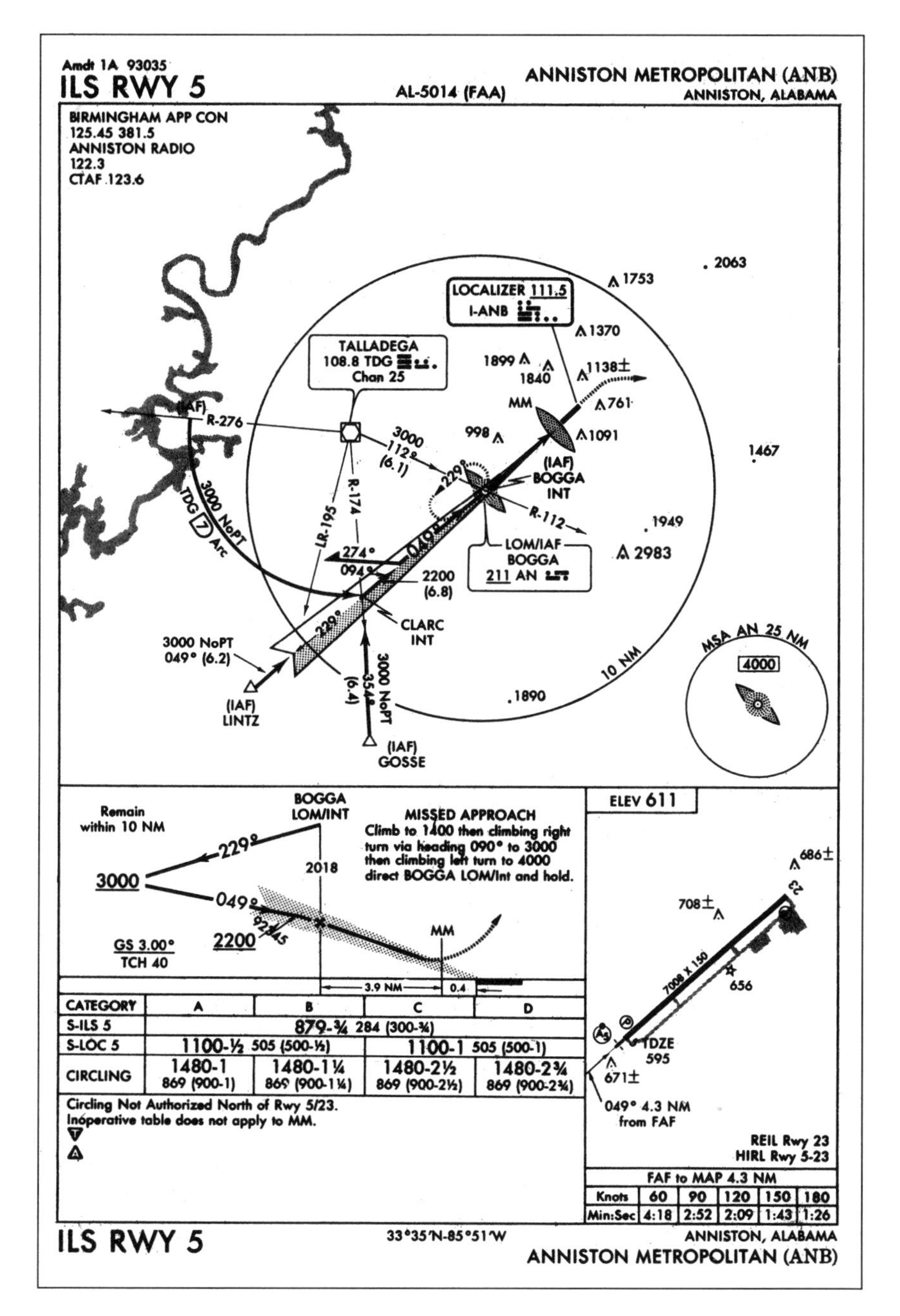

Since radar isn't available below 4000 feet, ATC can clear you to either the LOM for the procedure turn or to the VOR and out the radial to intercept the DME arc.

and requires advance planning as you must fly the arc to the runway. The missed approach is unconventional. If you use the second method for flying the arc, you must be alert to the step-down fixes, which require altitude changes while monitoring DME distance. We suggest using a combination of the first and second or first and third methods due to the importance of identifying the step-down fixes. As you get closer to the fixes, you might want to change the OBS to the step-down radial and adjust heading according to the DME indication.

Your clearance is, "Cleared to the Sloaf Intersection, maintain 2300 feet. Report established on the 14.7 DME arc. Cleared for the VOR/ DME Runway 14 approach to Martin State."

Suggested avionics set-up and management:

- #1 VOR/HSI - BAL Vortac 115.1, OBS 331 radial, DME - Hold.
- #2 VOR - BAL Vortac 115.1, OBS 65 radial (missed approach).

Since this is a right-hand (clockwise) arc, and your VOR doesn't have a 360-degree display, add 90 degrees to 331 to get your first heading after Sloaf. This should be 61°, which by inspection appears to be reasonably close to the arc as shown. Monitor the DME and radials, correcting heading as needed. Maintain 2300 feet.

After crossing Cumbe (R-018), descend to 1800 feet. Descend to 1200 feet after crossing Goves (R-036), the final approach fix.

After crossing the 45-degree radial, set the OBS to the 55-degree radial and descend to the MDA. Concentrate on bracketing the DME to at least within 0.5 nm of the 14.7 arc to ensure a good arrival at the runway.

The missed approach point is the 55-degree radial, where you must turn to intercept the 65-degree radial, which should be set-up on the #2 VOR.

After reaching 10.5 DME on the 65-degree radial, turn to 155° (65 + 90). This is your first heading as you monitor the radials and DME for the 11-mile arc. Change the #1 VOR to the BAL 105 radial and monitor the DME, radials and heading. You should end up on 195° when crossing Boast Intersection, depending on the wind.

Change the #2 VOR to OTT (113.7) and set the OBS to 39°. After crossing the BAL 105 radial, fly a teardrop entry (135°) to the hold.

The arc approach demands a high degree of proficiency. The most important elements are advance planning and maintaining a good cross-check. You'll need to refer to the charts often, so don't take your eyes away from the instruments longer than a split second or two at a time.

Positional Awareness

We'll close this book with a chapter discussing one of the most important skills in flying approaches (or, for that matter, in all of instrument flying): that of keeping track of where you are relative to where you need to be.

Without a firm idea of your location relative to the final approach course, navaids, intermediate fixes and the airport itself, you'll have a hard time completing the approach successfully. The process of interpreting the indications of our instruments and forming a clear picture of our location is one that is central to navigating under IFR.

There's really no "right" or "wrong" way to do this. Just how we perform the mental trick of transforming an altitude, a CDI indication, a heading and a TO/FROM flag reading into the fact that we're at a particular point in space is different for different pilots.

There are, of course, tricks to help you get there. Here are some.

Wheretheheckarewe?

You're approaching an airport served by radar when the controller assigns a heading and altitude for vectors to the final approach course. Since you no longer need the radios for en route navigation, it's good procedure to tune the primary nav radio to the final approach course and the secondary radio to identify any intermediate fixes. Once these navaids are tuned and identified, you're prepared for the time when you'll be cleared for the approach, and must resume your own navigation.

But, since you've set up all your nav radios to cover something that's going to happen in the future (namely the approach), you're now entirely in the hands of the controller. What if you lose comm? Have you any idea where you are?

In a sense, no, you don't, since your instruments are not set up to give you that information. But so long as you keep a clear mental picture of your location relative to some key points, you have a good idea of what to expect next. This makes flying any approach a whole lot easier.

Refer back to the first section of the book, dealing with precision approaches. There we went step-by-step through an ILS to Runway 16 at Westchester County Airport in White Plains, New York. All through the initial and intermediate segments of that approach, our hypothetical pilot had a very clear idea of his/her position relative to the final approach course, outer marker and airport. As a result, it was possible to think ahead and anticipate what would be required next.

While the CDI points to either side of the case and/or and the OFF flag is still in view, you should know your exact position relative to the approach course. Positional awareness, as it is commonly known, means keeping a constant mental picture of your aircraft in relation to a published course or navaid. Acquiring this skill can be lifesaving, especially during those rare occasions when a controller forgets about you during vectors, when you lose communications or when you get confused about your location.

Navigate Instead of Steer

The key to positional awareness is to stop thinking of the VOR as a steering instrument and to begin thinking of it as a navigational instrument. The CDI, whether tuned to a VOR or localizer, indicates the magnetic direction of any course.

For example, if the CDI indicates that a course is east of you, the aircraft is west of course. While this might seem obvious, the trick is learning how to instantly determine the direction of any radial.

Two 90-Degree Headings

Every VOR radial has two radials that are perpendicular to it. For example, the 180-degree radial has the 90- and 270-degree radials perpendicular to it. If you're not on the 180 radial, you're either east or west of it. A glance at the VOR indicator reveals your position.

Many VORs have a compass rose around the instrument face. The index for the selected radial is usually at the top and the reciprocal heading is at the bottom. The two perpendicular radials are on each side.

Using our example, when 180 is selected, 090 appears on the left side of the case and 270 appears on the right. The CDI always points in the direction of the radial. For instance, if the CDI points to the right (toward 270), the 180 radial is west of you.

This method works regardless of aircraft heading or indication of the TO/FROM flag. Believe it or not!

The trick of knowing where the radial is relative to you is key in maintaining positional awareness, and it's one of the tough concepts in instrument flight. Just try explaining it to a non-pilot sometime and see if you get anywhere.

Here's a test to see if you're catching on. Suppose you're tracking the final approach course inbound on a heading of 270. On your number two radio, you have Doubt Intersection dialed in, which is made up of the 180 degree radial of the PDQ VOR. The CDI points to the right side of the case. Is the intersection in front of you or behind you?

You don't need additional information to solve the problem and you shouldn't need to draw a map. If you can't visualize the VOR, draw one with 180 at the top, 360 at the bottom, 270 on the right side and 90 on the left. If the CDI points to the right side of the case, the radial is west of you. If you're heading west, the intersection is still in front of you.

Still confused? Here's the big hint. Remember that the *radial* is the "beam" that starts at the station and goes in the direction for which it's named (not really, but the analogy works). Typically, when we're tracking to a VOR along a radial we don't tune the radial, itself, but its reciprocal: The one going out the opposite side of the station. This is because it's the heading we're tracking that's important to us, not the radial we're on. Tuning the reciprocal makes the CDI indicate normally instead of in reverse, and gives us a "TO" flag. So, if we're tracking 360° to the station, we're on the 180° radial. We have 360 set on the OBS.

When it comes to intersections and positional awareness, however, we have to flop our thinking. It's the *radial* that's important, not the heading to the station. So we always dial up the appropriate radial.

Although we have only worked with cardinal headings, the principle is the same regardless. The direction to any radial is always found under the 90-degree index to which the CDI points. For example, if 327° is on the side of the case to which the CDI points, the radial you want to intercept is northwest of you. If this doesn't make sense, notice that 327° lies between north and west. Between north and west is northwest.

Whenever you need to know your position relative to the approach course, look at the 90-degree index. A comparison with the aircraft heading indicates whether the aircraft is traveling toward, away, or parallel to the approach course.

This might appear difficult to some of you and simple to others, but once mastered, you'll be able to figure the direction of any radial at a glance.

If it's still elusive, remember that all you need to know about where the VOR is *geographically* is on the face of the CDI: The radial, needle, and TO/FROM flag. To figure whether a radial is ahead of you, behind you, or off one wing or the other, you need one more piece of information: your heading. Think about it this way: Imagine you're in the middle of a room with the door in the middle of the north wall. It is north of you. Now close your eyes and spin around until you lose your sense of direction. Quick, and without opening your eyes: Where's the door? Answer: It's still directly north of you. You don't know your heading, since your eyes are still closed, but that's not important in terms of the geographical location of the door.

That situation is exactly like being on the 180 radial. You've got 180 on the OBS, and the flag reads FROM. You know you're on that line somewhere, but to know whether the VOR is ahead, behind, or to the side you need to know your heading. To fix your position two-dimensionally, you need a means of providing a cross-reference: DME, or a crossing radial.

Other Tricks

There are a few other tricks that can help with positional awareness. The most obvious, yet least often used, is to ask the man (woman) who knows where you are, even if you don't: the controller. If after a few vectors you find yourself disoriented, ask the controller to say your position. This has the two-fold advantage of reorienting you and reminding the controller that you're still out there.

It's standard procedure for the controller to state your position when issuing the clearance to intercept the final approach course. We find that few pilots pay much attention to this important bit of information.

If there's an NDB anywhere near the airport or the approach course, it should be tuned even if it isn't used on the approach. There are few things easier to interpret than a needle that points toward the airport or the outer marker. Sometimes it's necessary to look at another approach chart to find an NDB, since in order to reduce clutter on the chart, NDBs aren't usually depicted when they aren't part of the approach.

If the aircraft is equipped with loran, even if the installation isn't approved for IFR, it certainly wouldn't hurt to have the airport selected as a waypoint. Provided you're using other equipment for primary navigation, there's nothing illegal about using the loran as a cross-check, you just can't use it for primary navigation.

Although it's a good habit to set the inbound localizer heading on the VOR when flying an ILS, the CDI operates independently of where the heading is set. Older VOR and ILS indicators have a yellow and blue band on the bottom of the case, and you can glance at it to determine if you're on the yellow or the blue side of the airport.

Although we gained full compass cards around modern VOR indicators, we lost the blue and yellow markings. Now you need to remember, White is right. When the CDI points to the right side of the case, you're on the side of the approach course which is shown on the chart as the white side of the ILS course. By glancing at the CDI and comparing it to the chart, you can determine on which half of the localizer you're on.

It's easy to tune the radios and put yourself in the hands of ATC until intercepting final. With all the demands of instrument flying, vectors can provide a few moments rest so you can prepare yourself for the approach. But it's unwise to relinquish your authority as pilot in command. When on radar vectors, keep track of where you are and what's going on around you.

Clear Heads Prevail

The most important tool in maintaining your positional awareness is your old reliable gray matter. Bad weather, darkness, balky equipment, high workloads, and a host of other factors can all confuse you just enough to lose it. This has happened to most if not all of us at one time or another.

Think back to the last time you got "turned around." Remember the feeling of revelation when you suddenly realized where you were? Remember also how simple it seemed in hindsight?

It's common, when lost, for a pilot to overlook or ignore the blindingly obvious. Simple facts that would solve the problem are completely disregarded. Case in point: We had a student once who was approaching White Plains, where you need to call New York approach before entering the Class D area for clearance. We were coming in VFR.

The student called in "ten south, landing." Now, ten miles south of White Plains is right in the middle of the New York Class B area, and practically on top of LaGuardia. We were, of course, ten miles *north*, heading south. The student was thinking about the heading to fly, not our location.

The point is that if you become disoriented, a few seconds of objective thought will often clear up the problem and make it obvious where you really are. If you find yourself saying, "I think I'm south of the beacon, but that doesn't seem right..." stop and think for a moment: Is it possible for you to have gotten there?

Keeping track of your position isn't really difficult if you actively pay attention to it. And that's the key: You need to actively think about where you are, since when you're in IMC you don't have the simple and intuitive references that come from being able to see out the window. Once you master this skill, it will soon become second nature, and you'll be a better pilot for it.

Index

I

L

M

S

T

V